SO-AKI-507

**Penguin Education**
**Penguin Library of Physical Sciences**

**Inorganic Energetics**
W. E. Dasent

*Advisory Editor*
V. S. Griffiths

*General Editors*
Physics: N. Feather, F.R.S.
Physical Chemistry: W. H. Lee
Inorganic Chemistry: A. K. Holliday
Organic Chemistry: G. H. Williams

# Inorganic Energetics

W. E. Dasent

Penguin Books

Penguin Books Ltd, Harmondsworth,
Middlesex, England
Penguin Books Inc., 7110 Ambassador Road,
Baltimore, Md 21207, U.S.A.
Penguin Books Australia Ltd, Ringwood,
Victoria, Australia

First published 1970
Copyright © W. E. Dasent, 1970

Made and printed in Great Britain by
Bell and Bain Ltd, Glasgow
Set in Monotype Times New Roman

This book is sold subject to the condition that
it shall not, by way of trade or otherwise, be lent,
re-sold, hired out, or otherwise circulated without
the publisher's prior consent in any form of
binding or cover other than that in which it is
published and without a similar condition
including this condition being imposed on the
subsequent purchaser

# Contents

# Editorial Foreword

The chemistry section of the *Penguin Library of Physical Sciences* is planned to cover the normal content of honours degree courses of British universities, and those of comparable standard – C.N.A.A., Royal Institute of Chemistry, etc. Most of the optional subjects, which are becoming a prominent feature of present-day courses, will be included.

The series has been planned as a whole: nomenclature, the enumeration of tables and diagrams, and their layout, have been standardized throughout, so that there is a minimum of duplication. Every student will agree that an appreciable part of almost any modern textbook of organic or inorganic chemistry includes an account of atomic structure, wave mechanics, atomic and molecular orbitals, hybridization, etc., before making use of these concepts. This kind of duplication may be eliminated, in a uniform series, by frequent cross-referencing.

The subject has been subdivided so that students may buy the appropriate volumes as and when they become relevant to their course of study. Due to the introduction of optional subjects, and the advent of inter-disciplinary courses, not every student will require every volume. The outlay required, in any one year of the course, becomes realistic in present-day terms.

W. H. L.

# Preface

This book provides an elementary discussion of the energetic aspects of inorganic substances: the thermodynamic principles which underlie their formation in chemical reactions, their stabilities and their binding energies.

It is assumed that the reader has taken, or is taking concurrently, a course in elementary thermodynamics, and the book is in no way a substitute for such a course. Its purpose is rather to amplify those aspects of thermodynamics which are of particular interest to the student of inorganic chemistry and to provide a much wider selection of inorganic examples than is usually encountered in more general texts. Thus lattice energies, bond energies, ionization potentials, electron affinities and similar quantities are reviewed in some detail; melting, boiling and sublimation points are examined in thermodynamic terms, and much use is made of thermochemical cycles of the Born–Haber type to elucidate the various factors which contribute to the magnitude of the energy changes which accompany a wide variety of inorganic reactions.

It is hoped that the extensive tabulations of data included in the book will encourage the student to make his own energetic analyses of reactions which are not specifically discussed.

*Units.* The author of a book on energetics published in 1970 is faced with making a particularly difficult decision. Several years ago, few authors would have seen any problem; a year or two hence, one most fervently hopes, the position will be quite clear. But at this point in time the author's dilemma is a very real one. On the one hand he is encouraged, by those concerned with the development of a sensible, coherent and internationally acceptable system of units, to adopt units which conform to the Système International d'Unités, i.e. to use 'S.I. units'; on the other hand he is confronted by the stubborn fact that most of the major compilations of thermodynamic data, and a great deal of the existing chemical literature, use units which do not so conform. The case for S.I. units is admirably set out in such publications as *Physico-Chemical Quantities and Units* by M. L. McGlashan (Royal Institute of Chemistry, 1968). My decision has been to adopt S.I. units throughout the text, to include a brief explanatory section on S.I. units at the beginning of the book, and to seek the forbearance of readers who would have preferred the retention of the older units. In a transition period as uncomfortable as the present one, this decision has not been easily reached.

# Energy Units

The S.I. system uses units derived from the following basic set:

| Physical quantity | Name of unit | Symbol for unit |
|---|---|---|
| length | metre | m |
| mass | kilogramme | kg |
| time | second | s |
| electric current | ampere | A |
| thermodynamic temperature | kelvin | K |

Derived S.I. units for familiar energy quantities are as follows:

| Physical quantity | Name of unit | Symbol for unit | Definition of unit |
|---|---|---|---|
| energy | joule | J | $kg\,m^2\,s^{-2}$ |
| electric potential difference | volt | V | $kg\,m^2\,s^{-3}\,A^{-1}$ $= J\,s^{-1}\,A^{-1}$ |

Throughout this book, energy quantities are quoted in terms of S.I. units. In many cases the data have been converted from published sources in which they were given in non-S.I. units, such as the calorie. This should be borne in mind when referring to these sources. Although several varieties of calorie (e.g. the thermochemical calorie and the 15° calorie) have been in common use, the very small differences between them may be considered negligible for the purposes of this book. The relationships used to convert data from non-S.I. units were:

1 calorie (cal) = 4·184 joules (J),
    1 joule (J) = 0·2390 calorie (cal),
        1 erg = $10^{-7}$ joule (J).

In some chapters the *electron volt* (eV) is used. While the electron volt is not an S.I. unit, its use is 'permitted' within restricted contexts. The equivalents of the electron volt are expressed by the relationships:

1 electron volt (eV) (per atom) = 96·5 kilojoules per mole ($kJ\,mol^{-1}$)
                = 23·1 kilocalories per mole ($kcal\,mol^{-1}$).

# Chapter 1
# Energy Changes in Inorganic Reactions

## 1.1   Introduction

Knowledge of inorganic substances and their reactions has been greatly systematized by the recognition and classification of the sorts of forces which hold atoms together. Based on the nuclear model of the atom, and involving simple ideas of electron sharing and transfer, the largely qualitative 'electronic theory of valency' expounded by N. V. Sidgwick and others during the 1920s provided a new and more fundamental basis for the empirical framework of periodicity so strikingly demonstrated by Mendeleev and Lothar Meyer fifty years before. Such was the success of the early electronic theory, however, that for a long time many inorganic chemists were content to interpret the monovalency of sodium simply as a consequence of 'the stability of the valence octet' and to shrug off the rather bewildering chemistry of the transition elements as an unfortunate complication associated with their incomplete electron shells. Over the same period, chemists expert in thermodynamics had developed what seemed to be their own esoteric science in which quantities like $\Delta U$, $\Delta H$ and $\Delta G$ appeared, often enough in a context of heat engines, perfect gases adiabatically expanding and systems of weightless and frictionless pistons. The inorganic chemists, for their part, appeared to recognize the existence of reactions variously exothermic and endothermic, and of some reactions which did not 'proceed to completion', but otherwise pursued an essentially independent approach to chemistry.

Today, one of the features of modern inorganic chemistry is the willingness of its exponents to be quantitative. While it would be foolhardy to assert that there has been a happy and fruitful reconciliation of the points of view of the thermodynamicist and the inorganic chemist, the latter has certainly come to realize that the reactivity of the elements and compounds within his domain of interest can no longer be expressed in purely descriptive terms. Thus an attempt is made to afford statements like 'gold is an unreactive element', 'mercury compounds are easily reduced', 'the bonds in the iodine molecule are easily broken' or 'potassium chloride is a stable salt' the precision of a thermodynamic context. Inevitably such an attempt leads to a consideration of the *energy changes* which accompany not only laboratory-bench reactions, but also those which are not easily accessible experimentally, like

$$Na^+(g) + Cl^-(g) \rightarrow NaCl(s),$$

and those which, like

$$Hg(l) \rightarrow Hg(g),$$

are sometimes differentiated as 'physical' changes.

The term 'energy' is one which is widely and sometimes vaguely used. It is therefore important to be quite certain of the significance of the various thermodynamic quantities, notably $\Delta U$, $\Delta H$, $\Delta S$ and $\Delta G$, which are commonly encountered in quantitative descriptions of energy changes. The main purpose of this chapter is to introduce, discuss and illustrate these quantities.

## 1.2 The change in internal energy $\Delta U$

### 1.2.1 Absolute energy and energy changes

The total energy of a substance, called its *internal energy* and symbolized $U$, is the sum of all the different sorts of energy which a substance can be said to possess. Some of the components of the total energy can be precisely defined, while others still await recognition and definition.

For most of the purposes of chemistry – as distinct, say, from the purposes of nuclear physics – only those parts of the total energy which are susceptible to change in the course of chemical reactions are of interest. For example, the *nuclei* of atoms pass unchanged through purely chemical processes, so that any energy associated with the nucleus alone or with the particles which compose it, remains constant in quantity. Processes in which the nuclei are affected – such as radioactive emissions – are of course of interest to nuclear chemists and radiochemists but will not be discussed here. The only chemically significant components of the energy are therefore those associated with the translational, rotational and vibrational movements of the molecules (or other structural units capable of these types of motion) and with the various interactions, both intermolecular and intramolecular, which exist between positively charged nuclei and negatively charged electrons. The remainder of the energy not only remains constant but also resists any sort of complete and useful analysis.

The only significant – and indeed the only measurable – energy quantity is the *difference* between the energy of the products and the energy of the reactants for the reaction or process considered, that is, the energy change $\Delta U$:

$$\Delta U = U_{products} - U_{reactants}.$$

Nevertheless it is possible to recognize the *components* of the absolute energies (i.e. the components of $U_{products}$ and of $U_{reactants}$) which undergo change in chemical reactions, and it is therefore useful to discuss them. In particular, it is important to have a feeling for the relative *magnitudes* of the various components of the total energy, since some of them make only minor contributions to the total change in energy for chemical reactions conducted under ordinary conditions.

## 1.2.2 Components of the internal energy

*Translational energy* $U_{trans}$ is energy associated with translational motion in three dimensions. It is possessed (at temperatures above the absolute zero) only by chemical species capable of this sort of motion, like gas molecules (e.g. $H_2$) or atoms (e.g. He), and by the molecules in liquids. In the solid state translational energy is normally absent. Atoms and molecules free to move in three dimensions are said to possess three translational degrees of freedom.

*Rotational energy* $U_{rot}$ is energy associated with rotation about a centre of gravity, and is absent in monatomic gases (e.g. He). Diatomic gases (e.g. $H_2$, CO) and linear polyatomic gas molecules (e.g. HCN, $N_2O$, BrCN, $CO_2$) which rotate about two axes perpendicular to the line joining the nuclei are said to possess two rotational degrees of freedom and, at temperatures above the absolute zero, a corresponding rotational energy. In solids, the possibility of rotation depends on the crystal components and the nature of the bonding. For example, the non-polar molecules of solid nitrogen and hydrogen, and the ammonium ions in solid ammonium chloride, exhibit rotation. In cases where the components are locked in position by virtue of the crystal geometry (as in solid carbon dioxide) or by intermolecular bonding (as in ice or ammonium fluoride), rotational energy is either absent or of little significance.

*Vibrational energy* $U_{vib}$ is energy associated with the motion of the constituent atoms of a molecule (or polyatomic ion) towards and away from one another. Molecules possess $3n - 6$ vibrational degrees of freedom ($n$ = the number of atoms in the molecule) if they are non-linear, or $3n - 5$ vibrational degrees of freedom if they are linear. Vibrational energy is possessed by all diatomic and polyatomic molecules and ions in the gaseous, liquid and solid states. Crystals consisting of monatomic ions, like sodium chloride, exhibit only lattice vibrations, that is, vibrations of the crystal lattice as a whole. Unlike translational and rotational motions, which cease at 0 K, vibrational motion persists at this temperature and substances therefore possess a vibrational *zero-point energy*.

*Electronic energy* $U_{el}$ is energy associated with the interacting systems of positively charged nuclei and negatively charged electrons, in terms of which substances are adequately described for chemical purposes. (Note again that this description of matter would hardly satisfy a physicist, to whom the intimate structure of the nuclei is of great importance.) It is the change in electronic energy which commonly dominates the total energy change for a chemical reaction. Electronic energy has also been called 'chemical binding energy'; the general term 'bond energy' however is sometimes defined in such a way as to include translational, rotational and vibrational components. This is examined in section 1.3.1.

Translational, rotational and vibrational energies can be measured in relation to their values at 0 K, where $U_{trans} = 0$, $U_{rot} = 0$ and $U_{vib} =$ the zero-point energy. In the case of the electronic energy $U_{el}$ the choice of a

**15 The Change in Internal Energy $\Delta U$**

reference standard is more arbitrary. The electronic energy in the hydrogen molecule $H_2$, for example, can be assessed by comparing the energy of the $H_2$ molecule with either the energy of the infinitely separated nuclei and electrons (2 protons + 2 electrons) or, as is usually the case, the energy of the infinitely separated hydrogen atoms. In either case, the electronic energy of the hydrogen molecule $H_2$ is *lower* than the energy of the system chosen for comparison.

The relative magnitudes of the contributions made by $U_{trans}$, $U_{rot}$, $U_{vib}$ and $U_{el}$ can now be discussed.

### 1.2.3 *Quantization of the energy*

At the outset it must be noted that these various forms of energy are *quantized*, that is to say there exists for each sort of energy a range of permitted values or *energy levels*. The magnitude of the contribution of each sort of energy, therefore, will be determined by the extent to which each of the available energy levels is occupied under the conditions studied. This in turn depends on the size of the energy quanta: on the separations between the permitted levels, in a way which will be described in the next section. Experimental information about the sizes of energy quanta is most complete for isolated gas molecules free of intermolecular interactions, that is, for ideal gases.

Briefly, the sizes of translational quanta are minute, rotational quanta are of the order of $0.02 \text{ kJ mol}^{-1}$, vibrational quanta usually fall within the range $5$–$40 \text{ kJ mol}^{-1}$, while quanta of the electronic energy are commonly much larger.

Some typical energy quanta determined spectroscopically for the carbon monoxide (CO) molecule are as follows. The energy of the first allowed transition is shown in each case. The electronic transition corresponds to the excitation of an electron from a sigma-type bonding orbital ($x\sigma$) into a pi-type antibonding orbital ($v\pi$):

$$\Delta U / (\text{kJ mol}^{-1})$$

electronic:

$[KK(z\sigma)^2(y\sigma)^2(x\sigma)^2(w\pi)^4] \rightarrow [KK(z\sigma)^2(y\sigma)^2(x\sigma)^1(w\pi)^4(v\pi)^1]$     577

vibrational:     $v = 0 \rightarrow v = 1$                           25.1

rotational:      $J = 0 \rightarrow J = 1$                           0.046

### 1.2.4 *Components of the energy of an ideal gas*

The distribution of molecules of an ideal gas among the various energy levels depends on the size of the quanta in the following way:

If the number of molecules which occupy a given energy level $U_n$ is $N_n$, and the number of molecules which occupy the lowest level $U_o$ is $N_o$, then the difference between the two energy levels, that is the quantum absorbed in the transition $U_o \to U_n$, is $U_n - U_o$ and the ratio of molecules occupying the upper state to molecules occupying the lowest state $N_n/N_o$ is given by the Boltzmann expression

$$\frac{N_n}{N_o} = \exp\left[-\frac{U_n - U_o}{kT}\right],\qquad\qquad 1.1$$

where $k$ is Boltzmann's constant and $T$ is the absolute temperature. The ratio $N_n/N_o$ obviously depends on the size of the difference $U_n - U_o$ compared with the size of $kT$. The magnitude of $kT$ (and of its molar equivalent $RT$, $R$ is the gas constant) at various temperatures is as follows:

|  | $kT/(\text{J molecule}^{-1})$ | $RT/(\text{kJ mol}^{-1})$ |
|---|---|---|
| 0 K | 0 | 0 |
| 298 K (25°C) | $4 \cdot 12 \times 10^{-15}$ | $2 \cdot 48$ |
| 1273 K (1000°C) | $1 \cdot 76 \times 10^{-14}$ | $10 \cdot 58$ |

It is not difficult to deduce from **1.1** that, if $U_n - U_o$ is large compared with $kT$ (or with $RT$, if molar energies are considered), then the ratio $N_n/N_o$ is very small. This means that, for the sorts of energy whose level-spacings or quanta are much bigger than $kT$ (or $RT$), only the lowest level will be occupied to any significant extent. This is essentially the situation with the vibrational and electronic energies of most molecules.

For example, it has been stated above that vibrational quanta lie in the range 5–40 kJ mol$^{-1}$; if 25 kJ mol$^{-1}$ is chosen as a typical separation between the lowest vibrational level and the first excited level, then

$U_n - U_o = 25$ kJ mol$^{-1}$.

Since at room temperature (298 K) $RT = 2 \cdot 48$ kJ mol$^{-1}$,

$$\frac{U_n - U_o}{RT} = \frac{25}{2 \cdot 48} \simeq 10,$$

from which it follows that the ratio $N_n/N_o = 4 \cdot 5 \times 10^{-5}$, that is, for every 100 000 molecules in the lowest vibrational level (possessing only zero-point energy) there are only four or five in the first excited state (and still fewer in the higher levels).

For most molecules at room temperature the lowest electronic state is even more highly favoured.

The situation is quite different for translational and rotational levels. Rotational levels are separated by about 0·02 kJ mol$^{-1}$ for most molecules, and translational quanta are quite minute. In these cases many excited states will be extensively occupied at room temperature in addition to the lowest state. Indeed, in order to get estimates of the magnitudes of the translational and rotational energies of gases at room temperature, it may be assumed that the gases are ideal and that the energy is distributed classically, that is the energy is $\frac{1}{2}kT$ for each translational and rotational degree of freedom.

Since gas molecules possess three translational degrees of freedom, the translational energy $U_{trans}$ of a gas is $\frac{3}{2}kT$ per molecule, or $\frac{3}{2}RT$ per mole, which is 3·72 kJ mol$^{-1}$ at 298 K.

For linear molecules, which possess two rotational degrees of freedom, the rotational energy $U_{rot} = kT$ per molecule. or $RT$ per mole, which is 2·47 kJ mol$^{-1}$ at 298 K. For non-linear molecules, which possess three rotational degrees of freedom, the rotational energy $U_{rot} = \frac{3}{2}kT$ per molecule, or $\frac{3}{2}RT$ per mole, which is 3·72 kJ mol$^{-1}$ at 298 K.

*Example: hydrogen gas.* The significant components of the internal energy of a mole of hydrogen gas ($H_2$) at 298 K are as follows:

1. $U_{trans} = 3\cdot72$ kJ mol$^{-1}$.

2. $U_{rot} = 2\cdot47$ kJ mol$^{-1}$.

3. $U_{vib}$. It can be assumed that the $H_2$ molecule will be essentially in its lowest vibrational state at 298 K. This does not mean that its vibrational energy is zero, because all molecules retain one half-quantum of vibrational energy ($\frac{1}{2}h\nu_0$, where $h$ is Planck's constant and $\nu_0$ is the fundamental vibrational frequency) for each vibrational degree of freedom, even at the absolute zero of temperature. Since $H_2$ has only one vibrational degree of freedom ($3n-5=1$, when $n = 2$), its vibrational energy will be one half-quantum at 0°K, and close to this value at 298 K. The zero-point energy of $H_2$ is 26 kJ mol$^{-1}$. The zero-point energies of some other substances are shown in Table 1; the values were calculated from the experimental vibrational frequencies by taking one half of the energy for each fundamental and summing.

Table 1  Zero-point Energies (kJ mol$^{-1}$)

| $H_2$ | $N_2$ | $NH_3$ | $CH_4$ | $AsF_3$ | $BiCl_3$ | $SiF_4$ | $TiCl_4$ | NaCl | $KHF_2$ |
|---|---|---|---|---|---|---|---|---|---|
| 26 | 14 | 85 | 113 | 17 | 7 | 34 | 15 | 7·5 | 4·2 |

4. $U_{el}$. This is the energy associated with the interactions of the two protons and two electrons which constitute the hydrogen molecule. It can be conveniently measured as the difference between the energy of the $H_2$ molecule on the one hand, and two separated hydrogen atoms on the other, that is as $\Delta U$ for the reaction

$H_2(g) \rightarrow 2H(g)$.

If the reaction temperature were 0 K, then the energy change for the dissociation of $H_2$ molecules into atoms would be $\Delta U_0 = +432$ kJ (mol $H_2$)$^{-1}$ which represents the difference in energy between (a) one mole of $H_2$ molecules without translational or rotational energy but possessing the zero-point energy of vibration, and (b) two moles of hydrogen atoms without translational, rotational or vibrational energy; both the reactants and the products are assumed to be in their lowest electronic states.

$\Delta U_0$ for the above dissociation is normally called the 'bond-dissociation energy' (see section 4.1.1) of the hydrogen molecule. To obtain the true total of the electronic energy however (i.e. $\Delta U$ for the hypothetical dissociation in which translational, rotational and vibrational energies are completely absent from both the reactants and the products), the zero-point energy must be added to the experimental $\Delta U_0$,

i.e. $U_{el} = 432 + 26 = 458$ kJ (mol $H_2$)$^{-1}$.

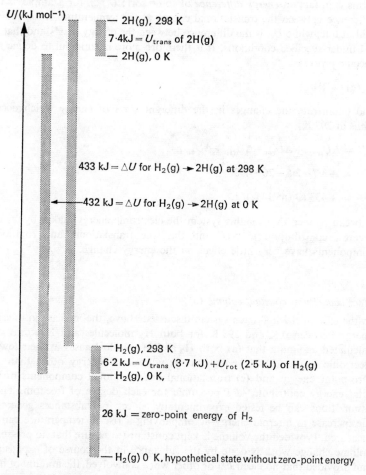

$U/(\text{kJ mol}^{-1})$

— 2H(g), 298 K

7·4 kJ = $U_{trans}$ of 2H(g)

— 2H(g), 0 K

433 kJ = $\triangle U$ for $H_2$(g) → 2H(g) at 298 K

432 kJ = $\triangle U$ for $H_2$(g) → 2H(g) at 0 K

— $H_2$(g), 298 K

6·2 kJ = $U_{trans}$ (3·7 kJ) + $U_{rot}$ (2·5 kJ) of $H_2$(g)

— $H_2$(g), 0 K,

26 kJ = zero-point energy of $H_2$

— $H_2$(g) 0 K, hypothetical state without zero-point energy

Figure 1  Internal energy differences for various states of the system $H_2$–2H (not to scale)

## 19  The Change in Internal Energy $\Delta U$

If the reaction temperature is 298 K, the experimental value for the change in internal energy on dissociation is $\Delta U_{298} = +433 \text{ kJ mol}^{-1}$, which differs only slightly from the value at 0 K.

The internal energy relationships for the $H_2$–2H system are summarized diagrammatically in Figure 1. It should now be clear that the representation of the total energy of the hydrogen molecule as a series of terms,

viz $\quad U_{\text{total}} = U_{\text{trans}} + U_{\text{rot}} + U_{\text{vib}} + U_{\text{el}}$,

is a device of limited value, as $U_{\text{total}}$ is in fact only that part of the energy susceptible to alteration in a chemical reaction and each of the contributing terms is in fact an *energy difference* of some sort: $U_{\text{trans}}$, for example, is the difference between the translational energy at the temperature specified and that at 0 K, while $U_{\text{el}}$ is the difference between the energy of $H_2$ and that of 2H under specified conditions. It is therefore more meaningful to define the specific process

$$H_2(g) \rightarrow 2H(g)$$

and enumerate the changes in the different sorts of energy which occur. Thus at 298 K,

$$\Delta U = \Delta U_{\text{trans}} + \Delta U_{\text{rot}} + \Delta U_{\text{vib}} + \Delta U_{\text{el}}$$

$$= +3{\cdot}7 - 2{\cdot}5 - 26 + 458$$

$$= +433 \text{ kJ (mol } H_2)^{-1}.$$

It can be seen that for this system the electronic energy makes by far the greatest contribution to $\Delta U$, and that the translational and rotational components have very little effect on the energy change.

### 1.2.5 *Heat capacity at constant volume $C_v$*

In the case of the hydrogen system discussed above, the increase in internal energy between 0 K and 298 K for both $H_2$ molecules and H atoms was calculated assuming that (a) both $H_2$ and H are ideal gases in their lowest electronic states, (b) $H_2$ possesses no vibrational energy other than the zero-point energy and (c) translational and rotational components of the total energy contribute $\frac{1}{2}RT$ per mole for each degree of freedom. These assumptions can be tested experimentally, since, for substances generally, the increase in internal energy accompanying a rise in temperature can be measured. Provided the volume is kept constant (to ensure that no pressure–volume change work is done by the substance in the course of expansion) and provided that no electrical or other work is involved, the amount of heat absorbed by a substance under these conditions is equal to the increase in internal energy. Thus the heat capacity at constant volume $C_v$ of a substance is the rate at which the internal energy changes with temperature,

i.e. $C_v = \left(\dfrac{\partial U}{\partial T}\right)_v$,

and is measured by determining experimentally the temperature rise which accompanies a given input of heat.

The values of the heat capacity $C_v$ at 298 K for a number of gases are listed in Table 2; these figures represent the heat absorbed (and thence the increase in internal energy) in J mol$^{-1}$, when the temperature rises by one kelvin at 298 K. Also shown are the 'theoretical' heat capacities: that is, for monatomic gases, the increase in $U$ will be wholly translational and equal to $\frac{3}{2}R$ per kelvin, which is 12·5 J mol$^{-1}$; for diatomic and linear polyatomic gases,

**Table 2** Heat Capacities $C_v$ at 298 K

| | $C_v/(\text{J K}^{-1}\,\text{mol}^{-1})$ experimental | $C_v/(\text{J K}^{-1}\,\text{mol}^{-1})$ 'theoretical' |
|---|---|---|
| He | 12·5 | 12·5 |
| Ar | 12·5 | 12·5 |
| $H_2$ | 20·5 | 20·8 |
| $O_2$ | 21·1 | 20·8 |
| $N_2$ | 20·7 | 20·8 |
| $Cl_2$ | 26 | 20·8 |
| CO | 20·8 | 20·8 |
| HCl | 21·0 | 20·8 |
| $CO_2$ | 29 | 20·8 |
| $N_2O$ | 31 | 20·8 |
| $SO_2$ | 31 | 25 |
| $NH_3$ | 27 | 25 |

the energy of two rotational degrees of freedom $(R)$ must be added, viz 12·5 + 8·3 = 20·8 J mol$^{-1}$; for non-linear polyatomic gases the rotational contribution is $\frac{3}{2}R$, so that the increase in $U$ = 12·5 + 12·5 = 25 J mol$^{-1}$. Some discrepancies between the experimental and calculated values are evident; they can be attributed to deviations from ideality, and to extra contributions of vibrational energy resulting from the existence of vibrational energy levels sufficiently low-lying to be significantly occupied at room temperature. Heat capacities, including those of solids and liquids, are discussed again for constant-pressure conditions in section 1.3.2.

**21 The Change in Internal Energy $\Delta U$**

## 1.3 The change in enthalpy or heat content $\Delta H$

### 1.3.1 *Relationship to the change in internal energy* $\Delta U$

A great many chemical reactions are carried out under conditions of constant pressure, that is in circumstances in which the amount of heat absorbed or evolved will reflect not only the change in internal energy, but also the amount of work done in the course of expansion or contraction, should a change of volume occur.

As long as no other sort of work is involved, the amount of heat absorbed or evolved under conditions of constant pressure is called the change in *enthalpy* or *heat content* and is symbolized by $\Delta H$.

Then $\Delta H = \Delta U + P\,\Delta V$,

where $P$ is the constant pressure and $\Delta V$ the volume change.

For example, for the reaction

$$H_2(g) \to 2H(g)$$

we have seen that $\Delta U$ at 298 K $= +433$ kJ (mol $H_2$)$^{-1}$ and this is equal to the heat absorbed if the reaction is carried out at constant volume. If the reaction is carried out at a constant pressure of one atmosphere and at 298 K the work done in doubling the volume against the constant pressure will be reflected in an additional absorption of heat. Then, if the gases are ideal,

$$P\,\Delta V = \Delta n\,.\,RT \qquad (\Delta n = \text{the change in the number of moles of gas})$$

and with $\Delta n = 1$,

$$P\,\Delta V = 1 \times 8 \cdot 31 \times 298 \cdot 2 \text{ J (mol } H_2)^{-1}$$

$$= 2 \cdot 5 \text{ kJ (mol } H_2)^{-1},$$

so that $\Delta H_{298} = \Delta U + P\,\Delta V$

$$= 433 + 2 \cdot 5$$

$$= 435 \text{ kJ (mol } H_2)^{-1}.$$

Since many reactions are carried out at room temperature (say 298 K) and in open vessels (i.e. at constant atmospheric pressure), the quantity $\Delta H_{298}$ is for some purposes of more interest than either $\Delta U_{298}$ or $\Delta U_0$.

The components of $\Delta H_{298}$ for the reaction $H_2(g) \to 2H(g)$ can now be set down. They are, in kilojoules per mole of hydrogen,

$$\Delta H_{298} = P\,\Delta V + \Delta U_{\text{trans}} + \Delta U_{\text{rot}} + \Delta U_{\substack{\text{zero-} \\ \text{point}}} + \Delta U_{\text{el}}$$

$$= +2 \cdot 5 + 3 \cdot 7 - 2 \cdot 5 - 26 + 458$$

$$= +435 \text{ kJ (mol } H_2)^{-1}.$$

## 22 Energy Changes in Inorganic Reactions

These figures are of interest because $\Delta H_{298}$ for an atomization reaction such as the above is commonly used as a measure of bond strength, the *thermochemical bond energy*, as discussed in section 4.1.2. When used in this way, it is salutary to remember that $\Delta H_{298}$ is a composite quantity, only one term of which – albeit the dominating one in the above instance, namely $\Delta U_{el}$ – is strictly a measure of what is usually acknowledged to be the essence of the bond itself: the interaction between electrons and nuclei. The terms $P\,\Delta V$, $\Delta U_{trans}$ and $\Delta U_{rot}$ are seldom of much significance numerically, but the contribution of the zero-point energy is often overlooked.

As will be seen in subsequent chapters, quantities commonly recorded as values of $\Delta H_{298}$ are, as their names imply, heats of formation (dealt with in the next section), heats of atomization (Chapter 4), and heats of sublimation and vaporization (Chapter 4). On the other hand, ionization energies (Chapter 2), electron affinities (Chapter 2), lattice energies (Chapter 3) and bond-dissociation energies (Chapter 4) may be tabulated as values of $\Delta U_0$. Quantities such as those quoted often appear in energy cycles used to elucidate various features of the reactivity of inorganic elements and compounds; where a low order of accuracy is acceptable, $\Delta U_0$ and $\Delta H_{298}$ are often used interchangeably, but in more refined calculations care should be taken to ensure consistency. This point will be referred to in later chapters.

1.3.2    *Heat capacity at constant pressure $C_p$*

The heat capacity at constant volume $C_v$ of a substance has already been described (section 1.2.5) as the rate of change of the internal energy $U$ with temperature. The heat capacity at constant pressure $C_p$ is the corresponding rate of change of the enthalpy $H$ with the temperature,

i.e.   $C_p = \left(\dfrac{\partial H}{\partial T}\right)_p$.

The factors contributing to the magnitude of $C_v$ for gases have already been discussed in section 1.2.5, and $C_p$ differs from $C_v$ only in that $C_p$ incorporates the variation with temperature of the pressure–volume work of expansion, assuming that this is the only sort of work involved, which is normally the case.

$C_p$ values at 298 K for a number of solids, liquids and gases are given in Table 3. It can be shown that for an ideal gas $C_p = C_v + R$, so that it is possible to calculate $C_p$ values using the assumptions presented in section 1.2.5; the calculated values are: monatomic gases, 20·8; diatomic and linear polyatomic gases, 29; non-linear polyatomic gases, 33 J K$^{-1}$ mol$^{-1}$. The data of Table 3 show that the $C_p$ values of gases are commonly higher (in some cases – e.g. $SiF_4$, $TiCl_4$ – considerably higher) than those calculated, and suggest that in these molecules there are substantial vibrational, and possibly electronic, contributions to the heat capacity at 298 K. For solids, where

**23   The Change in Enthalpy or Heat Content $\Delta H$**

**Table 3** Heat Capacities $C_p$ at 298 K

| | | $C_p/(\text{J K}^{-1}\,\text{mol}^{-1})$ |
|---|---|---|
| monatomic gases | | 20·8 |
| diatomic and polyatomic gases | $H_2$ | 29 |
| | $O_2$ | 29 |
| | $N_2$ | 29 |
| | $Cl_2$ | 34 |
| | $CO$ | 29 |
| | $HCl$ | 29 |
| | $CO_2$ | 37 |
| | $N_2O$ | 39 |
| | $SO_2$ | 40 |
| | $NH_3$ | 35 |
| | $SiF_4$ | 73 |
| | $BCl_3$ | 63 |
| | $H_2O$ | 33 |
| | $PF_3$ | 56 |
| | $TiCl_4$ | 96 |
| liquids | $AsCl_3$ | 133 |
| | $CCl_4$ | 134 |
| | $H_2O$ | 75 |
| | $Br_2$ | 72 |
| | $Hg$ | 28 |
| | $NaCl$ | 67 |
| | $SiCl_4$ | 140 |
| | $TiCl_4$ | 149 |
| solids | $Ag$ | 26 |
| | $C$ (graphite) | 8·7 |
| | $Cu$ | 24·5 |
| | $HgCl_2$ | 77 |
| | $I_2$ | 55 |
| | $KF$ | 50 |
| | $NaCl$ | 51 |
| | $P_4$ (white) | 94 |
| | $Se$ | 26 |
| | $SiO_2$ ($\alpha$-quartz) | 44 |
| | $TlCl$ | 53 |

translational (and usually rotational) motions are absent, the heat capacity reflects mainly the variation of vibrational energy with temperature. The heat capacity of a compound in the liquid phase is usually higher than that of either the solid or the gas, and does not respond to any simple theoretical treatment.

### 1.3.3 *Heats of formation and heats of reaction*

Enthalpy data for substances are commonly tabulated as *standard heats of formation*. The standard heat of formation at a specified temperature is the enthalpy change for the reaction in which one mole of the substance is formed isothermally from its elements in their standard reference states, with each of the reactants and products at a pressure of one atmosphere. The symbol for a standard heat of formation is $\Delta H_T^\circ$, where the superscript $^\circ$ refers to the condition of unit pressure, and the subscript $_T$ defines the absolute temperature. Very commonly standard heats of formation refer to a temperature of 298 K and are symbolized $\Delta H_{298}^\circ$, or sometimes simply $\Delta H_f^\circ$; the standard reference state for the elements from which the substance is formed is generally taken to be the stable form in which the element exists at one atmosphere pressure and 298 K.

For example, $\Delta H_f^\circ$, $HgCl_2(s) = -230 \text{ kJ mol}^{-1}$. This means that, when the reaction

$$Hg(l) + Cl_2(g) \rightarrow HgCl_2(s)$$

proceeds, and one mole of liquid mercury at one atmosphere pressure reacts with one mole of chlorine gas at one atmosphere pressure to give one mole of solid mercury (II) chloride under a pressure of one atmosphere, the temperature being maintained throughout at 298 K, the heat evolved is 230 kJ.

The heat of formation of the element itself in its standard state is of course zero.

The enthalpy change for any reaction can be calculated provided the heats of formation of the reactants and products are known.

E.g. for the reaction $\quad Ni(s) + 4CO(g) \rightarrow Ni(CO)_4(g)$,

$$\Delta H_f^\circ / (\text{kJ mol}^{-1}) \qquad 0 \qquad -110 \cdot 5 \qquad -605$$

$$\Delta H_{298}^\circ = \Delta H_f^\circ \text{ (products)} - \Delta H_f^\circ \text{ (reactants)}$$

$$= -605 \qquad -(0 + 4 \times -110 \cdot 5)$$

$$= -605 \qquad +442$$

$$= -163 \text{ kJ mol}^{-1}.$$

The use of $\Delta H$ as a measure of the difference in bond strengths of reactants and products is discussed in section 1.4.3. The way in which $\Delta H_f^\circ$ values for common compounds vary in the groups of the periodic table, and an analysis of the factors contributing to these variations, are described for ionic compounds in section 3.5, and for covalent compounds in section 4.3.

## 1.4 The change in free energy $\Delta G$

1.4.1 Of fundamental importance in chemistry is a quantity which will provide a measure of the extent to which a reaction between specified substances can occur under specified conditions. If the specified conditions are of constant temperature and pressure, then the thermodynamic quantity which provides such a measure is the change in *free energy* $\Delta G$ for the reaction. The free energy change is defined by the relationship

$$\Delta G = \Delta H - T\,\Delta S,$$

where $\Delta H$ is the change in enthalpy (discussed in the previous section 1.3), $T$ is the absolute temperature and $\Delta S$ is the change in *entropy*, the significance of which will be discussed in section 1.4.3.

For reactions in which the standard state condition is satisfied (see section 1.3.3) the symbols become for a specified temperature, $T$ K,

$$\Delta G^\circ = \Delta H^\circ - T\,\Delta S^\circ.$$

Tabulations of free energy data commonly quote values of $\Delta G_f^\circ$, the standard free energy of formation of a substance at 298 K. From such data free energy changes for reactions can be calculated.

E.g. for the reaction $CaS(s) + 2HCl(g) \rightarrow CaCl_2(s) + H_2S(g)$,

$\Delta G_f^\circ/(\text{kJ/mol}^{-1})$       $-477$    $-95\cdot3$      $-750$    $-33\cdot0$

$\Delta G_{298}^\circ = -750 + (-33\cdot0) - (-477) - 2(-95\cdot3)$

$\qquad\quad = -115 \text{ kJ (mol CaS)}^{-1}.$

This means that if the reaction were to proceed from left to right *to completion* with the pressure maintained at one atmosphere and the temperature at 298 K, then a decrease in free energy of 115 kJ mol$^{-1}$ would result.

*Entropy* data are usually tabulated as values of $S_{298}^\circ$, the entropy of the substance at 298 K, in joules per kelvin per mole. The change in entropy $\Delta S_{298}^\circ$ is then the sum of the entropies of the products minus the sum of the entropies of the reactants, as in the following examples:

$$Cl_2(g) + Ni(s) \rightarrow NiCl_2(s)$$

$S_{298}^\circ/(\text{J K}^{-1}\,\text{mol}^{-1})$     223     30     97

$\Delta S_{298}^\circ = 97 - 223 - 30$

$\qquad\quad = -156 \text{ J K}^{-1}\,\text{mol}^{-1}.$

$\Delta S^\circ$ can also, of course, be obtained from tabulated values of $\Delta G^\circ$ and $\Delta H^\circ$. For example, for the above reaction, $\Delta G^\circ_{298} = -259\,\mathrm{kJ\,mol^{-1}}$ and $\Delta H_{298} = -305\,\mathrm{kJ\,mol^{-1}}$:

$$\Delta G^\circ = \Delta H^\circ - T\,\Delta S^\circ,$$

therefore $\quad \Delta S^\circ = -\dfrac{\Delta G^\circ - \Delta H^\circ}{T}.$

Since $\quad \Delta G^\circ_{298} - \Delta H^\circ_{298} = -259 - (-305)$

$$= 46\,\mathrm{kJ} = 46\,000\,\mathrm{J},$$

$$\Delta S^\circ_{298} = -\frac{46\,000}{298 \cdot 2} = -155\,\mathrm{J\,K^{-1}\,mol^{-1}}.$$

It is of the utmost importance to appreciate the significance of the *sign* and *magnitude* of the free energy change for a reaction, and these will now be discussed.


1.4.2    *Significance of the sign and magnitude of* $\Delta G^\circ$

$\Delta G^\circ$ is simply a measure of the *equilibrium constant* $K$ for the reaction considered. The relationship between $\Delta G^\circ$ and $K$ is

$$\Delta G^\circ = -RT \ln K,$$

where $\Delta G^\circ$ is expressed in $\mathrm{J\,mol^{-1}}$, $R$ is the gas constant (in $\mathrm{J\,K^{-1}\,mol^{-1}}$) and $T$ is the absolute temperature.

If the reaction involves gases, then $K$ is the constant $K_p$, for which gas pressures are expressed in atmospheres. The case of reactions involving solutions is discussed in Chapter 5.

For reactions at 298 K, insertion of $T = 298 \cdot 2$ and $R = 8 \cdot 31$ into the equation $\Delta G^\circ = -RT \ln K$ and conversion to base 10 logarithms gives

$$\log_{10} K = -0 \cdot 000\,175\,\Delta G^\circ.$$

It is now easy to see how $K$ will be affected by the sign and magnitude of $\Delta G^\circ$:

If $\Delta G^\circ$ is negative, that is, if the reaction is accompanied by a decrease in free energy, then $\log_{10} K$ will be positive and $K > 1$.

If $\Delta G^\circ$ is positive, that is, if the reaction is accompanied by an increase in free energy, then $\log_{10} K$ will be negative and $K < 1$.

If no change in free energy occurs – if $\Delta G^\circ = 0$ – then $\log_{10} K = 0$ and $K = 1$.

Some values of $\log_{10} K$ and of $K$ itself for a range of values of $\Delta G^\circ$ are shown in Table 4.

**27   The Change in Free Energy** $\Delta G$

**Table 4**  Relations between Numerical Values of $\Delta G^{\circ}_{298}$, $\log_{10} K$ and $K$ at 298 K

| $\Delta G^{\circ}_{298}$/kJ | $\log_{10} K$ | $K$ |
|---|---|---|
| −500 | 87·5 | $3\cdot2 \times 10^{87}$ |
| −200 | 35·0 | $1\cdot0 \times 10^{35}$ |
| −100 | 17·5 | $3\cdot2 \times 10^{17}$ |
| −50 | 8·75 | $5\cdot6 \times 10^{8}$ |
| −20 | 3·50 | $3\cdot2 \times 10^{3}$ |
| −10 | 1·75 | 56 |
| −5 | 0·875 | 7·5 |
| −1 | 0·175 | 1·5 |
| 0 | 0 | 1 |
| 1 | $\bar{1}\cdot825$ | 0·67 |
| 5 | $\bar{1}\cdot125$ | 0·13 |
| 10 | $\bar{2}\cdot25$ | 0·018 |
| 20 | $\bar{4}\cdot50$ | $3\cdot2 \times 10^{-4}$ |
| 50 | $\bar{9}\cdot25$ | $1\cdot8 \times 10^{-9}$ |
| 100 | $\overline{18}\cdot5$ | $3\cdot2 \times 10^{-18}$ |
| 200 | $\overline{35}\cdot0$ | $1\cdot0 \times 10^{-35}$ |
| 500 | $\overline{88}\cdot5$ | $3\cdot2 \times 10^{-88}$ |

It can be seen from Table 4 that the equilibrium constant $K$ rapidly becomes very large as $\Delta G^{\circ}$ becomes increasingly negative, and that $K$ rapidly becomes very small as $\Delta G^{\circ}$ becomes increasingly positive. The precise significance of the numerical value of $K$ will of course depend on the form of the equilibrium constant expression, that is on the powers to which the concentrations of the various reactants and products are raised. However, remembering that in such an expression the products are always contained in the numerator and the reactants in the denominator, then in general the value of $\Delta G^{\circ}$ need only be moderately negative to signify a reaction in which, at equilibrium, there is a considerable preponderance of product molecules. Similarly, a moderately large positive value of $\Delta G^{\circ}$ signifies a reaction in which, at equilibrium, there is a corresponding preponderance of reactant molecules. It is only in the case of reactions for which $\Delta G^{\circ}$ is zero, or close to zero, that both reactants and products may be present at equilibrium in comparable proportions.

The standard free energy change $\Delta G^{\circ}$ is thus a measure of the *energetic feasibility* of a reaction, *under the specified and restricted conditions to which the symbol $\Delta G^{\circ}_T$ refers*; it may not however give any indication of energetic feasibility under *other* conditions. Furthermore, the sign and magnitude of $\Delta G^{\circ}$ indicate the proportions of reactants and products which will be present *once equilibrium is achieved*, but indicate *nothing* about the *rate* at which equilibrium is achieved. The following examples illustrate some of the possible dangers inherent in attaching to the sign of $\Delta G°$ more than its due significance:

(a) *If $\Delta G°$ for a reaction is negative, the reaction may still not proceed because the rate of reaction is very slow.* There are innumerable examples of reactions which, in spite of quite highly negative values of $\Delta G°$, do not proceed to a detectable extent for kinetic reasons. A few examples involving familiar substances are as follows:

(i) The decomposition of nitric oxide gas into its elements,

$$NO(g) \rightarrow \tfrac{1}{2}N_2(g) + \tfrac{1}{2}O_2(g) \qquad \Delta G°_{298} = -86\cdot7 \text{ kJ (mol NO)}^{-1}.$$

The equilibrium constant $K_p$, deduced from $\Delta G°_{298}$, is

$$K_p = \frac{p_{N_2}^{\frac{1}{2}} p_{O_2}}{p_{NO}} = 1\cdot55 \times 10^{15},$$

which indicates that, at equilibrium, the dissociation of nitric oxide gas into its elements would be virtually complete. It is well known, of course, that nitric oxide is quite stable at room temperature with respect to decomposition into its elements: this is because its *rate* of decomposition is too slow to be observed.

(ii) The hydrolysis of carbon tetrachloride,

$$CCl_4(l) + 2H_2O(l) \rightarrow CO_2(g) + 4HCl(g)$$
$$\Delta G_{298} = -232\cdot3 \text{ kJ (mol CCl}_4)^{-1}.$$

It thus appears that at room temperature carbon tetrachloride is thermodynamically unstable with respect to hydrolysis; its observed stability must therefore be due to kinetic factors.

(iii) The reaction of metals with oxygen gas. Many of the common metals (e.g. Fe, Al, Cr) form oxides whose free energies of formation are quite highly negative:

| | $\Delta G_f°/(\text{kJ mol}^{-1})$ |
|---|---|
| $Al_2O_3$ | $-1576$ |
| $Cr_2O_3$ | $-1047$ |
| $Fe_2O_3$ | $-741$ |

These metals are therefore thermodynamically unstable in air; their apparent stability in bulk arises from a variety of non-thermodynamic factors and is commonly due to the presence of a thin surface film of oxide which makes further reaction extremely slow.

**29   The Change in Free Energy $\Delta G$**

(b) *If $\Delta G°$ for a reaction is negative, the reaction may still not proceed because another possible product is more highly favoured for energetic reasons.* For example, suppose it is desired to prepare lead(IV) oxide by treatment of lead(II) sulphide with hydrogen peroxide:

$$PbS(s) + 4H_2O_2(l) \rightarrow PbO_2(s) + SO_2(g) + 4H_2O(l).$$

Since $\Delta G°_{298}$ for this reaction is $-919 \text{ kJ mol}^{-1}$, the reaction is thermodynamically possible. However, $\Delta G°$ for the alternative reaction

$$PbS(s) + 4H_2O_2(l) \rightarrow PbSO_4(s) + 4H_2O(l)$$

is even more highly negative, $\Delta G°_{298} = -1211 \text{ kJ mol}^{-1}$, and this is the reaction which in fact occurs. The difference between the two values of $\Delta G°_{298}$ is of course the free energy change for the reaction

$$PbO_2(s) + SO_2(g) \rightarrow PbSO_4(s) \qquad \Delta G°_{298} = -292 \text{ kJ mol}^{-1}.$$

(c) *If $\Delta G°$ for a reaction is positive, the reaction may still proceed under different conditions.* For example, for the reaction

$$CrCl_3(s) + \tfrac{1}{2}H_2(g) \rightarrow CrCl_2(s) + HCl(g)$$

at 298 K, $\Delta G°_{298} = +20 \text{ kJ mol}^{-1}$,

hence $\quad K_p = \dfrac{p_{HCl}}{p_{H_2}^{\frac{1}{2}}} = 3.0 \times 10^{-4}$,

that is at equilibrium the amount of hydrogen chloride present (and hence the amount of chromium(III) chloride reduced) would be very small. However, for the same reaction at 1000 K, $\Delta G°_{1000} = -52 \text{ kJ mol}^{-1}$ and $K_p = 5.7 \times 10^2$. It is obviously energetically feasible to reduce chromium(III) chloride with hydrogen at 1000 K, and in this case an increase in the temperature of about 700 K is sufficient to reverse the energy balance of the reaction. Even at temperatures when the *equilibrium* proportion of hydrogen chloride is small, it might still be possible to carry out the reduction by 'sweeping' with hydrogen gas, continually displacing the equilibrium in the direction of the products by removing hydrogen chloride as it is formed.

(d) *If $\Delta G°$ for a reaction is positive, the required product may still be obtained by using different reactants.* For example, $\Delta G°_f$ for chlorine monoxide $Cl_2O$ is $+94 \text{ kJ mol}^{-1}$, that is, for the reaction

$$Cl_2(g) + \tfrac{1}{2}O_2(g) \rightarrow Cl_2O(g),$$

$\Delta G°_{298} = +94 \text{ kJ mol}^{-1}$ and the equilibrium constant

$$K_p = \frac{p_{Cl_2O}}{p_{Cl_2} \, p_{O_2}^{\frac{1}{2}}} = 3.7 \times 10^{-17},$$

from which it is clear that chlorine monoxide cannot be prepared from its elements under standard conditions at 298 K. This does not mean that it cannot be prepared at all; for example, for the reaction

$$HgO(s) + 2Cl_2(g) \rightarrow HgCl_2(s) + Cl_2O(g),$$

$\Delta G^{\circ}_{298} = -33 \text{ kJ mol}^{-1}$, and chlorine monoxide can in fact be prepared in this way. Although it is thermodynamically unstable with respect to its elements, its rate of decomposition is sufficiently slow to permit its storage for some time. In this respect chlorine monoxide is similar to nitric oxide NO which, in spite of its thermodynamic instability with respect to its elements (discussed in (a) above) can easily be prepared by other means, for example from nitrous acid and iron(II) sulphate solution.

(e) *If $\Delta G^{\circ}$ for a reaction is positive, it may be possible to force the reaction to proceed, for example by supplying the required energy electrolytically.* For example, the decomposition of molten lithium chloride into lithium metal and chlorine gas will obviously not proceed spontaneously at 1000 K:

$$LiCl(l) \rightarrow Li(l) + \tfrac{1}{2}Cl_2(g) \qquad \Delta G^{\circ}_{1000} = +324 \text{ kJ (mol LiCl)}^{-1}.$$

This and many other reactions of the same sort can of course be *made* to proceed by the application of an e.m.f. of appropriate magnitude and direction, that is by electrolysis.

### 1.4.3 *Factors contributing to the sign and magnitude of $\Delta G^{\circ}$*

As explained above, reactions which are energetically feasible are those for which the sign of the free energy change is negative. Since the free energy change is the resultant of a heat or enthalpy term and an entropy term,

$$\Delta G = \Delta H - T\Delta S,$$

it follows that the sign of $\Delta G$ will be determined by the signs and magnitudes of the terms $\Delta H$ and $T\Delta S$. It will be seen later that for many reactions at ordinary temperatures, $T\Delta S$ makes only a small contribution, and the enthalpy change is the dominating term. However, in general, both $\Delta H$ and $T\Delta S$ must be taken into account.

Clearly if $\Delta H$ is negative (i.e. if the reaction is exothermic) and at the same time $\Delta S$ is positive (if an entropy increase occurs), then $\Delta G$ must inevitably be negative and the reaction energetically feasible. Similarly $\Delta G$ will be positive (and the reaction not feasible on energetic grounds) when an endothermic reaction (positive $\Delta H$) is accompanied by an entropy loss ($\Delta S$ negative). In cases where $\Delta H$ and $\Delta S$ have the same sign, then the sign of $\Delta G$ will depend on the relative magnitudes of the contributions of $\Delta H$ and $T\Delta S$. Reactions illustrating these various possibilities are as follows:

|  | $\Delta H^\circ_{298}$ /(kJ mol$^{-1}$) | $T\Delta S^\circ_{298}$ /(kJ mol$^{-1}$) | $\Delta G^\circ_{298}$ /(kJ mol$^{-1}$) |
|---|---|---|---|

1. exothermic reaction with
   entropy increase:
   $2O_3(g) \rightarrow 3O_2(g)$

   | $-285$ | $+42$ | $-327$ |
   |---|---|---|
   | favourable | favourable | favourable |

2. endothermic reaction with
   entropy decrease:
   reverse of (1)

3. exothermic reaction outweighed by entropy de-
   crease:
   $3H_2S(g) + N_2(g)$
   $\rightarrow 2NH_3(g) + 3S(\text{rhombic})$

   | $-32$ | $-98$ | $+66$ |
   |---|---|---|
   | favourable | unfavourable | unfavourable |

4. endothermic reaction outweighed by entropy in-
   crease:
   reverse of (3)

5. exothermic reaction not
   outweighed by entropy
   decrease:
   $H_2(g) + \frac{1}{2}O_2(g) \rightarrow H_2O(l)$

   | $-286$ | $-49$ | $-237$ |
   |---|---|---|
   | favourable | unfavourable | favourable |

6. endothermic reaction not
   outweighed by entropy
   increase:
   reverse of (5)

It follows from the above that the factors which tend to make a reaction 'go' (i.e. which tend to make $\Delta G$ negative) are:
1. a decrease in enthalpy (negative $\Delta H$), and
2. an increase in entropy (positive $\Delta S$).
   It is helpful to express each of these factors in a more descriptive way.

*The enthalpy contribution, $\Delta H$.* A convenient view to take of $\Delta H$ is that it is a measure of the difference between products and reactants in respect of *total bond strength*. According to this view, the total bond strength of the reactants (or products) is the *total heat of atomization* of the reactants (or products). Thus, an exothermic reaction is one in which the bonds in the products are collectively *stronger* than those in the reactants, while an endothermic reaction is one in which the bonds in the products are collectively *weaker* than those in the reactants. Examples:

(a) The reaction

$$\tfrac{1}{2}H_2(g) + \tfrac{1}{2}F_2(g) \rightarrow HF(g)$$

is exothermic; $\Delta H^\circ_{298} = -269$ kJ (mol HF)$^{-1}$.

That $\Delta H^\circ_{298}$ is a bond-strength difference is evident from the following scheme:

$$\tfrac{1}{2}H_2(g) + \tfrac{1}{2}F_2(g) \rightarrow HF(g)$$

$\Delta H^\circ_{298}$ | 218 | 79 | 566 kJ mol$^{-1}$

H(g)   F(g)   H(g)+F(g)

heat absorbed in     reactants    products
breaking bonds:    $218 + 79 = 297$   566 kJ mol$^{-1}$

Clearly the bonds in the products are stronger than those in the reactants by $566 - 297 = 269$ kJ mol$^{-1}$, and $\Delta H_{298}$ for the reaction is $-269$ kJ mol$^{-1}$.

(b) For reactions involving solids, liquids and solutions the view of $\Delta H$ as a measure of the bond-strength difference between products and reactants is only valid as long as the term 'bond' is taken to include all attractive interactions, both intermolecular and intramolecular.

For example, the reaction

$$\tfrac{1}{4}P_4(s,\text{ white}) + 1\tfrac{1}{2}Cl_2(g) \rightarrow PCl_3(l)$$

is exothermic: $\Delta H^\circ_{298} = -311$ kJ mol$^{-1}$.

Total bond strength of reactants:

| | $\Delta H^\circ_{298}/(\text{kJ mol}^{-1})$ |
|---|---|
| (i) $\tfrac{1}{4}P_4(s,\text{ white}) \rightarrow \tfrac{1}{4}P_4(g)$ | $+59$ |
| (ii) $\tfrac{1}{4}P_4(g) \rightarrow P(g)$ | $+256$ |
| (iii) $1\tfrac{1}{2}Cl_2(g) \rightarrow 3Cl(g)$ | $+363$ |
| | $+678$ |

Bond strength of product:

| | |
|---|---|
| (iv) $PCl_3(l) \rightarrow PCl_3(g)$ | $+32$ |
| (v) $PCl_3(g) \rightarrow P(g) + 3Cl(g)$ | $+957$ |
| | $+989$ |

Note that the heat absorbed in reactions (i) and (iv) is required for the fission of *intermolecular* (van der Waals) bonds.

## 33 The Change in Free Energy $\Delta G$

The bonds in the products are thus collectively stronger than those in the reactants by $989 - 678 = 311$ kJ mol$^{-1}$, and $\Delta H_{298}$ for the reaction is $-311$ kJ mol$^{-1}$.

(c) Even when 'ionic' substances are involved, the bond-strength difference must still be measured in terms of heats of *atomization*, as in the following example:

$$Na(s) + \tfrac{1}{2}Cl_2(g) \rightarrow NaCl(s) \qquad \Delta H^\circ_{298} = -411 \text{ kJ mol}^{-1}.$$

Total bond strength of reactants:

|  |  | $\Delta H^\circ_{298}$ /(kJ mol$^{-1}$) |
|---|---|---|
| $Na(s)$ | $\rightarrow Na(g)$ | $+108$ |
| $\tfrac{1}{2}Cl_2(g)$ | $\rightarrow Cl(g)$ | $+121$ |
| $Na(s) + \tfrac{1}{2}Cl_2(g) \rightarrow Na(g) + Cl(g)$ | | $+229$ |

Bond strength of product:

|  |  |  |
|---|---|---|
| $NaCl(s)$ | $\rightarrow Na^+(g) + Cl^-(g)$ | $+770$ |
| $Na^+(g) + e \rightarrow Na(g)$ | | $-495$ |
| $Cl^-(g) - e \rightarrow Cl(g)$ | | $+365$ |
| $NaCl(s)$ | $\rightarrow Na(g) + Cl(g)$ | $+640$ |

As measured by the over-all heats of atomization, the bonds in the product are stronger than those in the reactants by $640 - 229 = 411$ kJ mol$^{-1}$, which is $-\Delta H^\circ_{298}$ for the reaction.

**Table 5** Entropies of Fusion, Vaporization and Sublimation $\Delta S^\circ_T$ for solid–liquid transitions (fusion)

| Substance | m.p. $T/K$ | $\Delta S^\circ_T/$(J K$^{-1}$ mol$^{-1}$) |
|---|---|---|
| NaCl | 1074 | $+27$ |
| SiCl$_4$ | 203 | 38 |
| TeF$_6$ | 235 | 37 |
| Ne | 25 | 14 |
| Al | 659 | 11 |
| Cl$_2$ | 172 | 37 |
| SiH$_4$ | 89 | 7 |
| N$_2$O | 182 | 36 |
| Pt | 2028 | 11 |
| H$_2$O | 273 | 22 |

$\Delta S_T^\circ$ for liquid–gas transitions (vaporization)

| Substance | b.p. $T/K$ | $\Delta S_T^\circ/(\text{J K}^{-1}\,\text{mol}^{-1})$ |
|---|---|---|
| $Br_2$ | 332 | +94 |
| Hg | 630 | 94 |
| $TiCl_4$ | 410 | 88 |
| AgCl | 1837 | 97 |
| $P_4$ | 553 | 94 |
| Na | 1155 | 86 |
| $PCl_3$ | 348 | 88 |
| $AsF_3$ | 331 | 90 |
| $H_2O$ | 373 | 110 |
| $NH_3$ | 240 | 97 |

$\Delta S_{298}^\circ$ for solid–gas transitions (sublimation)

| Substance | $\Delta S_{298}^\circ/(\text{J K}^{-1}\,\text{mol}^{-1})$ |
|---|---|
| Ag | +130 |
| NaF | 166 |
| $HgCl_2$ | 150 |
| $I_2$ | 144 |
| RbBr | 152 |

**Table 6** Entropy Changes for Reactions in Which Gaseous Products are Formed from Solid or Liquid Reactants at 298 K

| Reaction | $\Delta S_{298}^\circ$ $/(\text{J K}^{-1}\,\text{mol}^{-1})$ | $T\,\Delta S_{298}^\circ$ $/(\text{kJ mol}^{-1})$ |
|---|---|---|
| $1\tfrac{1}{2}Br_2(l) + \tfrac{1}{4}P_4(s) \rightarrow PBr_3(g)$ | +75 | +22 |
| $Li(s) + \tfrac{1}{2}I_2(s) \rightarrow LiI(g)$ | 146 | 44 |
| $C(graphite) + 2S(rhombic) \rightarrow CS_2(g)$ | 168 | 50 |
| $H_2O(l) \rightarrow H_2(g) + \tfrac{1}{2}O_2(g)$ | 163 | 49 |
| $NaCl(s) \rightarrow Na(g) + Cl(g)$ | 243 | 74 |
| $NH_4Cl(s) \rightarrow NH_3(g) + HCl(g)$ | 285 | 85 |

**35 The Change in Free Energy $\Delta G$**

**Table 7** Entropy Changes for Reactions in Which There is an Increase in the Number of Gaseous Particles at 298 K

| Reaction | $\Delta S^{\circ}_{298}$ /(J K$^{-1}$ mol$^{-1}$) | $T \Delta S^{\circ}_{298}$ /(kJ mol$^{-1}$) |
|---|---|---|
| $BiCl_3(g) \rightarrow Bi(s) + 1\frac{1}{2}Cl_2(g)$ | $+34$ | $+10$ |
| $PbO_2(s) \rightarrow PbO(s) + \frac{1}{2}O_2(g)$ | 94 | 28 |
| $Pb_3O_4(s) \rightarrow 3PbO(s) + \frac{1}{2}O_2(g)$ | 95 | 28 |
| $SiCl_4(l) + 2H_2O(l) \rightarrow SiO_2(s) + 4HCl(g)$ | 410 | 122 |
| $ZnS(s) + 2H_2O(l) \rightarrow Zn(OH)_2(s) + H_2S(g)$ | 91 | 27 |
| $PbCO_3(s) \rightarrow PbO(s) + CO_2(g)$ | 151 | 45 |
| $NaCl(s) \rightarrow Na(s) + \frac{1}{2}Cl_2(g)$ | 90 | 27 |
| $PH_3(g) \rightarrow P(s, \text{ white}) + 1\frac{1}{2}H_2(g)$ | 30 | 9 |
| $KHF_2(s) \rightarrow KF(s) + HF(g)$ | 136 | 41 |
| $AsF_3(l) \rightarrow As(s, \text{ grey}) + 1\frac{1}{2}F_2(g)$ | 159 | 47 |

**Table 8** Entropy Changes for Gas-phase Reactions at 298 K in Which No Change Occurs in the Number of Gas Particles

| Reaction | $\Delta S^{\circ}_{298}$ /(J K$^{-1}$ mol$^{-1}$) | $T \Delta S^{\circ}_{298}$ /(kJ mol$^{-1}$) |
|---|---|---|
| $H_2(g) + F_2(g) \rightarrow 2HF(g)$ | $+14$ | $+4$ |
| $H_2(g) + Cl_2(g) \rightarrow 2HCl(g)$ | 20 | 6 |
| $H_2(g) + Br_2(g) \rightarrow 2HBr(g)$ | 21 | 6 |
| $H_2(g) + I_2(g) \rightarrow 2HI(g)$ | 21 | 6 |
| $N_2(g) + O_2(g) \rightarrow 2NO(g)$ | 25 | 8 |
| $Br_2(g) + Cl_2(g) \rightarrow 2BrCl(g)$ | 11 | 3 |
| $I_2(g) + Cl_2(g) \rightarrow 2ICl(g)$ | 11 | 3 |
| $NO(g) + Cl_2(g) \rightarrow NOCl(g) + Cl(g)$ | $-5$ | $-1$ |

*The entropy contribution, $T \Delta S$.* Is it possible to make reasonably confident predictions of the likely sign of $\Delta S^{\circ}$, and hence to decide whether the entropy change will tend to assist ($\Delta S^{\circ}$ positive) or hinder ($\Delta S^{\circ}$ negative) the progress of the reaction under consideration? A search for the answer to this question is best initiated by a consideration of some experimental results ($\Delta S^{\circ}_{298}$ values) for reactions involving gases under standard conditions.

Tables 6 to 9 collect $\Delta S^{\circ}_{298}$ values for reactions which all involve the formation of at least some gas-phase molecules or atoms. Table 9, for example, exemplifies gas-phase reactions which involve the formation of a bigger number of gas particles. $\Delta S^{\circ}_{298}$ and $T \Delta S^{\circ}_{298}$ are positive (i.e. the entropy has increased) in all cases. The $\Delta S^{\circ}_{298}$ values of Tables 6 and 7 show that in all the quoted reactions where the number of gas-phase particles in the products is greater than the number in the reactants (whatever the nature or phase of the other reactants or products may be) an entropy *increase* is again general. The gas-phase reactions of Table 8 however are those in which the number of product particles is the same as the number of reactant particles. In these cases it is striking that the entropy change is very small indeed; $T\Delta S^{\circ}_{298}$ is close to zero and of the order of 5 kJ mol$^{-1}$.

These experimental results strongly suggest an important and useful empirical generalization: *an increase in the number of gaseous particles in the course of a reaction conducted at constant temperature and pressure tends to give rise to an increase in entropy, that is a positive value of $\Delta S^{\circ}_{298}$.*

**Table 9** Entropy Changes for Gas-phase Reactions at 298 K in Which There is an Increase in the Number of Gas-phase Particles

| Reaction | $\Delta S^{\circ}_{298}$ /(J K$^{-1}$ mol$^{-1}$) | $T\Delta S^{\circ}_{298}$ /(kJ mol$^{-1}$) |
|---|---|---|
| $O_2(g) \rightarrow 2O(g)$ | +117 | +35 |
| $NH_3(g) \rightarrow \frac{1}{2}N_2(g) + 1\frac{1}{2}H_2(g)$ | 99 | 30 |
| $P_4(g) \rightarrow 4P(g)$ | 372 | 111 |
| $S_8(g) \rightarrow 8S(g)$ | 916 | 273 |
| $NO_2(g) \rightarrow \frac{1}{2}N_2(g) + O_2(g)$ | 60 | 18 |
| $N_2O_4(g) \rightarrow N_2(g) + 2O_2(g)$ | 297 | 89 |
| $H_2O(g) \rightarrow H_2(g) + \frac{1}{2}O_2(g)$ | 44 | 13 |
| $Ni(CO)_4(g) \rightarrow Ni(g) + 4CO(g)$ | 572 | 171 |

One is naturally led to inquire why this should be so. Clearly the standard entropy $S^{\circ}_{298}$ of a gas must be high. The reasons for this originate in the discussion of the quantized energy levels of ideal gas molecules given in sections 1.2.2–4, and can be developed along the following lines:

The entropy of an ideal gas at a given temperature is determined by the number and spacing of the various electronic, vibrational, rotational and translational energy levels available to the gas. In general, the more distinct ways there are of distributing the molecules throughout the range of available energy levels, the higher will be the entropy. (The entropy may also be affected by configurational or spatial effects and these are discussed at a later stage). For example, if for some particular component of the energy the quanta are so large that only the ground state is occupied under the given conditions, then there is only one way of assigning the molecules: they all belong to the ground state, and there will be no contribution to the entropy in respect of that particular sort of energy. If on the other hand one imagines

**37    The Change in Free Energy** $\Delta G$

a hypothetical situation in which (a) for some component $E$ of the energy, a number of equally and closely spaced accessible levels exist, and (b) a sample of four molecules are assigned to these levels, then the following five distributions all give rise to the same total for $E$:

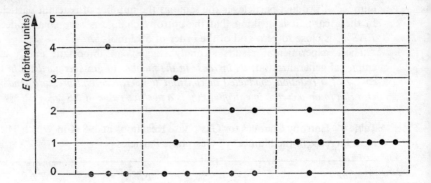

In this simplified situation there are five distinct ways of distributing the molecules among the available energy levels; when the energy is spread over a range of quantized levels in this way, a positive contribution to the entropy results.

Thus the very existence of a wide range of *accessible* energy levels will tend to generate entropy; this is particularly so in the case of the closely spaced rotational levels and *a fortiori* the translational levels of the ideal gas under consideration.

It is possible to divide the entropy of an ideal gas into components corresponding to the vibrational, rotational and translational contributions:

$$S^{\circ}_{298} = S^{\circ}_{vib} + S^{\circ}_{rot} + S^{\circ}_{trans}.$$

It is assumed that all the particles are in their ground electronic state.

Thus for $CO_2(g)$, the components are

$$S^{\circ}_{298} = 2 + 55 + 157$$

$$= 214 \text{ J K}^{-1} \text{ mol}^{-1}.$$

It is noteworthy that the entropy is dominated by the translational contribution, with a sizable contribution of rotational entropy. The vibrational component is very small, indicating that most of the $CO_2$ molecules are in their ground vibrational state. Hence it is not difficult to understand why in a reaction such as the gas-phase atomization of carbon dioxide (in which the number of gas-phase particles increases), the entropy *increases* by a substantial amount:

$$CO_2(g) \rightarrow C(g) + 2O(g)$$

$S^\circ_{298}/(\text{J K}^{-1}\text{ mol}^{-1})$      214     158    $2 \times 161$

$\Delta S^\circ_{298} = +266 \text{ J K}^{-1}$

In this reaction, which yields monatomic products, there is a loss of rotational and vibrational degrees of freedom (i.e. rotational and vibrational levels disappear), while many new translational levels will become available. Hence the entropies of C(g) and O(g) are wholly translational, and the large increment in translational entropy in the course of the reaction is only slightly offset by the loss of rotational and vibrational entropy consequent upon the formation of monatomic reaction products.

Just as high entropies are observed for gases, so the entropies of the corresponding *solids* at the same temperature are low. In a crystal, translational degrees of freedom are normally absent; so, too, are rotational degrees of freedom, except in those cases where constituents of the crystal (for example, the $NH_4^+$ ions in $NH_4Cl$) are free to rotate. Normally the only thermal energy in a solid is of the vibrational sort, arising from vibrations of the lattice itself (as in sodium chloride) or of the component molecules or polyatomic ions if they are present. Hence when a solid sublimes (see Table 5),

e.g.   $I_2(s) \rightarrow I_2(g)$    $\Delta S^\circ_{298} = 144 \text{ J K}^{-1}\text{ mol}^{-1}$,

or dissociates into gaseous products,

e.g.   $NH_4Cl(s) \rightarrow NH_3(g) + HCl(g)$    $\Delta S^\circ_{298} = 285 \text{ J K}^{-1}\text{ mol}^{-1}$,

the large increases in entropy arise essentially from the appearance in the products of new and relatively closely spaced rotational and translational energy levels over which the thermal energy can be spread.

When a solid melts, the constituents of the resulting liquid, although they are still in contact, exhibit translational and rotational movement, and (unless they are monatomic) vibrational movement as well. It is therefore not surprising that entropy *increases* during isothermal fusion processes, as the data of Table 5 show. The values of $\Delta S^\circ_{\text{fusion}}$ are however not very large, and usually much smaller than entropies of vaporization (Table 5), which are remarkably constant (about 95 J K$^{-1}$ mol$^{-1}$ at the boiling point). Entropies of fusion and vaporization are discussed further for ionic compounds in section 3.6 and for covalent compounds in section 4.4. The positive values of $\Delta S^\circ_T$ for fusion, vaporization and sublimation processes are of course an inevitable consequence of the fact that these processes are endothermic ($\Delta H^\circ$ positive) and reversible when carried out under equilibrium conditions;

i.e.   $\Delta S^\circ = \dfrac{\Delta H^\circ}{T}$,

and if $\Delta H^\circ$ is positive, so too must be $\Delta S^\circ$.

# 39 The Change in Free Energy $\Delta G$

The foregoing discussion of entropy changes has been couched entirely in terms of *thermal* entropy, that is entropy generated by the spreading of thermal energy over the available energy levels. It is now necessary to consider what has been termed *configurational* or *spatial* entropy. In assessing the spread of thermal energy it is necessary to take into account the distribution of the particles among the available energy levels for each *distinguishable* arrangement of the particles in space. For example, in a crystal composed of a single sort of atom or molecule, there is normally only *one* geometrical arrangement of the components compatible with a given value of the total energy. In certain cases, however, this is not so. For example the carbon monoxide molecule CO has a very small dipole moment and closely resembles the non-polar iso-electronic nitrogen molecule $N_2$ in many ways, including shape and size. In the carbon monoxide crystal, therefore, it is possible that the molecules may arrange themselves with their dipoles pointing either way (i.e. CO $\cdots$ OC or CO $\cdots$ CO) without sensibly affecting the total energy. There are thus many different ways of arranging the molecules in the crystal lattice, whose entropy is thereby increased by an additional configurational component.

A further example is the isothermal fusion of a crystal composed of very long chain (e.g. hydrocarbon) molecules. In the solid state the molecules are held in rigidly defined positions in the crystal lattice. With the freedom of movement conferred by melting, however, the long molecules are able to curl up in many alternative ways in the liquid state. The entropies of fusion of such substances are often particularly high, because of the additional configurational component.

*Aqueous solutions.* The above discussion is restricted to the entropy changes for reactions involving *pure substances* under standard conditions. Where *solutions* are involved, the considerations which must be taken into account are distinctly more complex. For example, when a crystalline, ionic solid dissolves in water under standard conditions, a superficial view of the process may lead one to predict an inevitable increase in entropy, for what appears to occur is simply the transformation of the components of the crystal from their rigidly defined positions in a crystal lattice into an environment where new translational and rotational degrees of freedom may be acquired. This view, of course, neglects to take into account the effect of the solution process on the solvent itself. The ions of the crystal lattice certainly become free-moving, but certain of the water molecules (which on the average have substantial freedom of movement in the pure solvent) become locked in position in the course of hydrating the dissolving ions and thus lose their independent translational capacity – this effect in itself will tend to *decrease* the entropy. There are thus, in the solution process, a number of tendencies which have opposing effects on the direction of the entropy change, and it is not always easy to predict which effect will predominate.

For example, when sodium iodide dissolves in water,

$$NaI(s) \rightarrow Na^+(aq) + I^-(aq),$$

$S^\circ_{298}/(J\,K^{-1}\,mol^{-1})$      91      60      109

the entropy change is positive; $\Delta S^\circ_{298} = 78\,J\,K^{-1}\,mol^{-1}$, while for the solution of magnesium chloride,

$$MgCl_2(s) \rightarrow Mg^{2+}(aq) + 2Cl^-(aq),$$

$S^\circ_{298}/(J\,K^{-1}\,mol^{-1})$      89      -118      $2 \times 55$

there is a decrease in entropy; $\Delta S^\circ_{298} = -97\,J\,K^{-1}\,mol^{-1}$. This result suggests that the effect of the bipositive ion $Mg^{2+}$ in restricting the degrees of freedom of water molecules is quite profound. A good deal of care and circumspection is therefore necessary in seeking qualitative explanations of the sign of $\Delta S^\circ$ for reactions in solution. The entropies of aqueous ions are discussed further in Chapter 5.

Finally, it must be noted that the whole of this section has been confined to reactions occurring at a constant and specified temperature and pressure. There are traps for the unwary in the case of reactions conducted adiabatically a much-quoted example of which is the crystallization of a supercooled liquid. Superficially one might expect that the entropy would *decrease*, since the process is a liquid $\rightarrow$ solid transformation; however, the potential energy released when the crystal lattice is formed is not lost as heat as would be the case in isothermal crystallization, but is retained to increase the thermal (in this case vibrational) energy of the solid. The spreading of this extra energy over the vibrational levels in the crystal results in a net increase in entropy.

1.4.4    *Relative magnitudes of $\Delta H$ and $T \Delta S$*

Most reactions which occur spontaneously at room temperature and atmospheric pressure are exothermic, that is they are reactions in which the entropy term $T \Delta S$, if negative, is too small to outweigh the negative value of $\Delta H$. Relatively few are endothermic; it is not common for an unfavourable (positive) value of $\Delta H$ to be outweighed by a favourable (positive) contribution from the term $T \Delta S$, at ordinary temperatures. As temperatures increase, however, the contribution of the enthalpy term $\Delta H$, which commonly dominates $\Delta G$ at room temperature, is gradually outweighed by an increasingly significant contribution from $T \Delta S$. The reason for this is straightforward. Both $\Delta H$ and $\Delta S$ are temperature-dependent quantities, but in general they do not change very much with temperature unless a phase change is involved. It is not $\Delta S$ itself however which contributes to $\Delta G$, but the product of $\Delta S$ and the absolute temperature $T$. For a kilokelvin rise in temperature say, $\Delta S$ may not be affected much, but $T \Delta S$ will increase considerably. For example, the simple atomization reaction

$$F_2(g) \rightarrow 2F(g)$$

**41**    **The Change in Free Energy** $\Delta G$

does not proceed spontaneously at 298 K because the heat absorbed in breaking the covalent bonds in the diatomic $F_2$ molecules,

$$\Delta H^\circ_{298} = +158 \text{ kJ (mol } F_2)^{-1},$$

is too great to be overcome by the favourable entropy change accompanying the formation of fluorine atoms,

$$\Delta S^\circ_{298} = +115 \text{ J K}^{-1} \text{ mol}^{-1}$$

($T \Delta S^\circ_{298}$, with $T = 298 \cdot 2$ K, is $+34$ kJ mol$^{-1}$), so that the free energy change is positive:

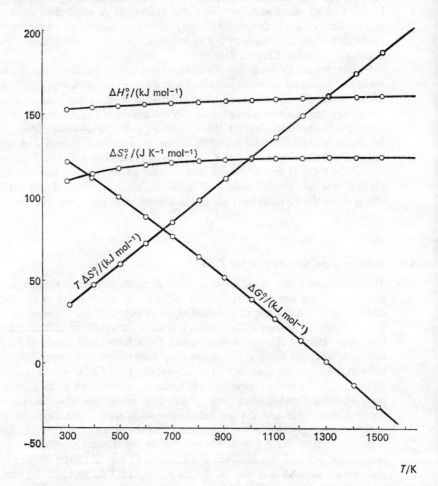

Figure 2  Variation with temperature of $\Delta H^\circ$, $\Delta S^\circ$, $T\Delta S^\circ$ and $\Delta G^\circ$ for the reaction $F_2(g) \rightarrow 2F(g)$

**42    Energy Changes in Inorganic Reactions**

$$\Delta G^{\circ}_{298} = \Delta H^{\circ}_{298} - T\,\Delta S^{\circ}_{298}$$
$$= +158 - 34$$
$$= +124 \text{ kJ (mol } F_2)^{-1}.$$

At 1500 K, however, although the enthalpy change,

$$\Delta H^{\circ}_{1500} = +167 \text{ kJ (mol } F_2)^{-1},$$

and the entropy change, $\Delta S^{\circ}_{1500} = +128$ J K$^{-1}$ mol$^{-1}$, do not differ very much from the values at 298 K, the term $T\Delta S^{\circ}_{1500}$, with $T = 1500$ K, is now 192 kJ mol$^{-1}$, so that the free energy change is negative:

$$\Delta G^{\circ}_{1500} = \Delta H^{\circ}_{1500} - T\,\Delta S^{\circ}_{1500}$$
$$= +167 - 192$$
$$= -25 \text{ kJ (mol } F_2)^{-1},$$

that is the spontaneous dissociation of $F_2$ molecules is energetically feasible at 1500 K.

The variation of $\Delta H^{\circ}$, $\Delta S^{\circ}$, $T\,\Delta S^{\circ}$ and $\Delta G^{\circ}$ with temperature are plotted in Figure 2.

It follows that, in accordance with observation, transitions such as solid $\rightarrow$ liquid, liquid $\rightarrow$ gas, complex molecules $\rightarrow$ simple molecules and gas molecules $\rightarrow$ gas atoms, all of which are characterized by positive values of $\Delta H^{\circ}$ (since they all involve breaking bonds, either intermolecular or intramolecular) and positive values of $\Delta S^{\circ}$, are more likely, on energetic grounds, to proceed at higher temperatures, where the term $T\,\Delta S^{\circ}$ is more likely to outweigh the unfavourable (positive) $\Delta H^{\circ}$ term.

### 1.4.5 *Estimation of* $\Delta G$, $\Delta H$ *and* $\Delta S$

The energetic feasibility of a specified reaction can be determined from a knowledge of $\Delta G$, which in turn can be evaluated from a knowledge of $\Delta H$ and $\Delta S$. The required heat and entropy data may not, however, be available, either because the necessary experiments may not have been done, or because one or more of the substances involved may never have been prepared. The latter possibility is encountered when it is desired to verify the energetic feasibility of a proposed preparative method for some new compound. The *estimation* of $\Delta H$ and $\Delta S$ is then necessary. Procedures for carrying out estimations vary according to the type of substance considered, and are discussed for ionic compounds in Chapter 3, and for covalent compounds in Chapter 4.

### 1.5 Sources of thermodynamic data for inorganic substances

The major compilations of the thermodynamic (enthalpy, entropy, free energy and heat capacity) data used and referred to in this book are as follows:

**43    Sources of Thermodynamic Data for Inorganic Substances**

1. *Selected Values of Chemical Thermodynamic Properties*, National Bureau of Standards (U.S.A.) Circular 500, Government Printing Office, Washington, D.C., 1952. This standard work is in the course of revision, and two volumes incorporating the revisions have been published by the National Bureau of Standards:
*Selected Values of Thermodynamic Properties, Part 1, Tables for the first 23 elements in the standard order of arrangement*; Technical note 270–1, 1965; *Part 2, Tables for the elements 24 through 32 in the standard order of arrangement*; Technical note 270–2, 1966.

2. Landolt-Börnstein, 4. Teil, *Kalorische Zustandsgrössen*, Springer-Verlag, Berlin, 1961.

3. Useful single-volume works are:
(a) W. M. Latimer, *Oxidation Potentials*, 2nd edn, Prentice-Hall, 1952.
This book contains extensive tabulations of $\Delta G_f^\circ$, $\Delta H_f^\circ$, $S_{298}^\circ$ and $E^\circ$ values. It incorporates many of the data of the unrevised 1952 National Bureau of Standards Circular 500 (1, above), and many of Latimer's estimates. Unfortunately the sign convention used for $E^\circ$ values is not that recommended by the International Union of Pure and Applied Chemistry.
(b) O. Kubaschewski, E. L. Evans and C. B. Alcock, *Metallurgical Thermochemistry*, 4th edn, Pergamon Press, 1967.
(c) G. N. Lewis and M. Randall, *Thermodynamics*, revised by K. S. Pitzer and L. Brewer, 2nd edn, McGraw-Hill, 1961, contains in its appendixes a small but useful collection of carefully selected data.
(d) The article 'Lattice energies' by T. C. Waddington in *Advances in Inorganic Chemistry and Radiochemistry* (H. J. Emeleus and A. G. Sharpe, eds.), vol. 1, Academic Press, 1959, is a definitive review of this field and contains extensive tabulations of lattice energies.
See also 'Lattice energy and associated properties' by W. H. Lee and M. F. C. Ladd, in *Progress in Solid State Chemistry*, (H. Reiss, ed.), vols. 1 to 3, Pergamon Press, 1960, 1962, 1964.
(e) T. L. Cottrell, *The Strengths of Chemical Bonds*, 2nd edn, Butterworths, 1956, is a critical compilation and discussion of bond energies.

# Chapter 2
# Energetics of Gaseous Atoms and Ions

## 2.1 Gas-phase atoms

In some respects gas-phase atoms are not of great chemical interest, since of the hundred-odd elements known, only six – the noble gases: helium, neon, argon, krypton, xenon and radon – occur naturally as gaseous atoms at ordinary temperatures and pressures. Hence for most elements, monatomic species are encountered only in reactions at elevated temperatures, or possibly as short-lived reaction intermediates. However the energy change involved when gaseous atoms are formed from the parent standard-state element is important since it provides a measure of the strength of the bonding in the parent element; furthermore the energy changes which accompany the gain and loss of electrons by the gas-phase atoms are important theoretical quantities. This chapter is devoted to a discussion of energy changes such as these.

## 2.2 The formation of gaseous atoms M(g) from elements in their standard states

The changes in enthalpy $\Delta H^\circ_{298}$ which occur when the monatomic gas is formed from the element in its standard state at 298 K, that is for the process

M(standard state) $\rightarrow$ M(g)

are shown in Table 10.

For those elements – the non-metals – in whose standard states the bonding is covalent, the heat of atomization is a measure of the covalent bond strength; the bond energies derived from such data are discussed in Chapter 4. It is convenient to discuss the remaining elements, which are essentially metallic, at this stage.

### 2.2.1 The heats of atomization of metals

The heat of atomization of a metal, $\Delta H^\circ_{\text{atom}}$, represents the heat absorbed when the solid metal (for mercury, the liquid metal) is converted into separate gas-phase atoms at 298 K and a pressure of one atmosphere. As discussed in section 1.3, $\Delta H^\circ_{298}$ incorporates both a small $P \Delta V$ term and the small difference between M(s) and M(g) in respect of translational and vibrational energy, but essentially it is a measure of the strength of the bonds between the metal atoms in the standard state.

**Table 10** Heats of Atomization at 298 K from Elements in Their Standard States, $\Delta H^\circ_{298}$/(kJ mol$^{-1}$)

| 1 | 2 | 3 | 4 | 5 | 6 | 7 | 8 | 9 | 10 | 11 | 12 | 13 | 14 | 15 | 16 | 17 |
|---|---|---|---|---|---|---|---|---|---|---|---|---|---|---|---|---|
| H 218 | | | | | | | | | | | | | | | | |
| Li 161 | Be 326 | | | | | | | | | | | B 565 | C 715 | N 473 | O 249 | F 79 |
| Na 108 | Mg 149 | | | | | | | | | | | Al 324 | Si 452 | P 315 | S 278 | Cl 121 |
| K 90 | Ca 177 | Sc 326 | Ti 473 | V 515 | Cr 397 | Mn 281 | Fe 416 | Co 425 | Ni 430 | Cu 339 | Zn 126 | Ga 272 | Ge 372 | As 287 | Se 207 | Br 112 |
| Rb 82 | Sr 164 | Y 410 | Zr 611 | Nb 774 | Mo 659 | Tc 649 | Ru 669 | Rh 577 | Pd 381 | Ag 286 | Cd 111 | In 244 | Sn 301 | Sb 259 | Te 192 | I 107 |
| Cs 78 | Ba 178 | La 435 | Hf 703 | Ta 781 | W 837 | Re 791 | Os 728 | Ir 690 | Pt 566 | Au 368 | Hg 61 | Tl 180 | Pb 197 | Bi 207 | Po 145 | At 92 |
| | Ra 130 | | Th 571 | | U 523 | | | | | | | | | | | |

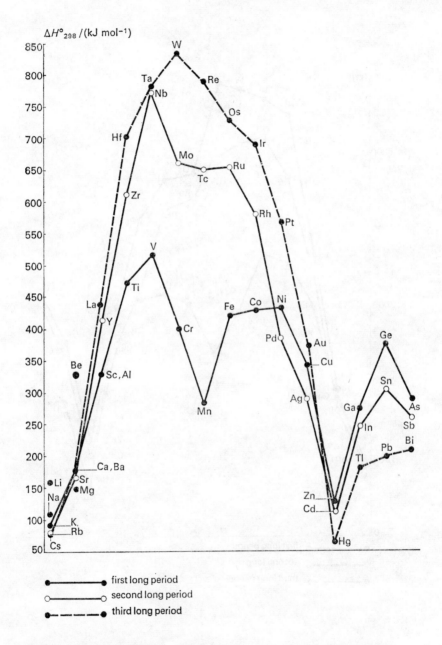

Figure 3   Heats of atomization of metals, $\Delta H^{\circ}_{298}$ for M(s) → M(g)

**47   The Formation of Gaseous Atoms from Elements**

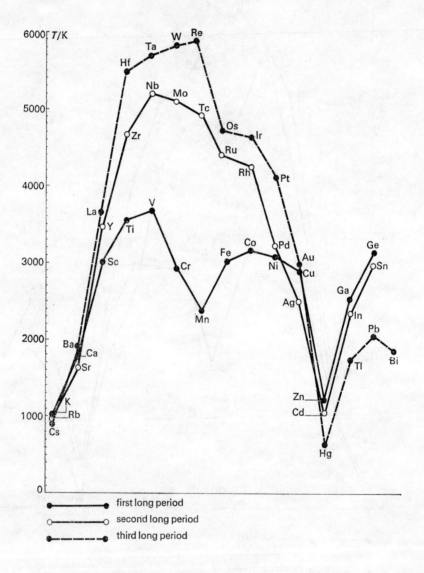

Figure 4   Boiling points of metals (K)

## 48   Energetics of Gaseous Atoms and Ions

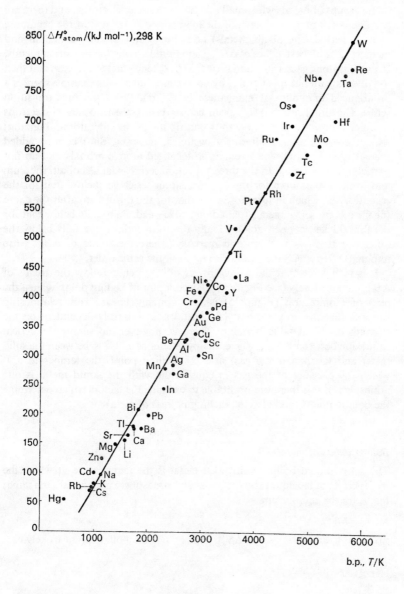

Figure 5 Relation between boiling point (*T*/K) and the heat of atomization $\Delta H^{\circ}_{atom}$ of metals at 298 K

## 49 The Formation of Gaseous Atoms from Elements

The way in which $\Delta H^{\circ}_{atom}$, and thence the strength of the metallic bonding, varies within the periodic table is shown in Figure 3. The lowest values occur in the groups of metals with small numbers of valence electrons, and there are two consistent minima in each of the long periods – the first at the beginning of each period (the alkali metals) and the second at zinc, cadmium and mercury. The highest values of $\Delta H^{\circ}_{atom}$ are found among the transition metals. In passing along each transition series, $\Delta H^{\circ}_{atom}$ tends first to increase and then to fall off again, but this trend is by no means regular – for example there is a pronounced minimum at manganese in the middle of the first transition series. The initial rise in $\Delta H^{\circ}_{atom}$ can be ascribed to the tendency of electrons to enter $d$-orbitals singly and thus contribute to the interatomic bonding; when the $d$-orbitals are all singly occupied, however, the electrons added thereafter form pairs which remain in localized atomic orbitals and do not participate in bonding. In the three transition series as far as cobalt, rhodium and iridium, the curve for the first transition series lies below that for the second series, which in turn lies below that for the third; thereafter the curve for the second-series metals (palladium, silver, cadmium) falls below that for the first (nickel, copper, zinc). Finally the third-series curve falls below the other two at zinc, cadmium and mercury (where the values of $\Delta H^{\circ}_{atom}$ are minimal) after which the values rise again in the same order.

It is interesting that the *boiling points* of the metals follow the trends of $\Delta H^{\circ}_{atom}$ quite closely (see Figure 4); indeed a plot of boiling point against the heat of atomization (Figure 5) is very roughly linear. This relationship suggests that the boiling point of a metal is very largely dependent on the strength of the metallic bonding. There is, however, no simple theoretical connexion between $\Delta H^{\circ}_{atom}$ (the enthalpy difference at 298 K between the solid metal and its monatomic gas) and the boiling point (the temperature at which the pressure of the gas in equilibrium with the liquid metal is one atmosphere). It is therefore profitable to examine the factors which determine the boiling points (and also the melting points) of metals.

### 2.2.2 *Boiling points of metals*

The conventional boiling point of a metal is the temperature at which the free energies of the liquid and the gas at one atmosphere pressure are the same; that is for the equilibrium

$M(l) \rightleftharpoons M(g)$,

$\Delta G^{\circ}_{b.p.} = 0$, and $\Delta H^{\circ}_{b.p.} = T \Delta S^{\circ}_{b.p.}$, where $T$ is the boiling point in kelvins.

Hence   $T = \dfrac{\Delta H^{\circ}_{b.p.}}{\Delta S^{\circ}_{b.p.}}$,

that is the boiling point (in kelvins) is the quotient of the heat of vaporization and the entropy of vaporization. The values of $\Delta H^{\circ}_{b.p.}$ and $\Delta S^{\circ}_{b.p.}$ for the metals are listed in Table 11. The values of $\Delta H_{b.p.}$ – essentially a measure of the strength of the metallic bonding in the liquid metal – range from between 50 and 100 kJ mol$^{-1}$ (sodium, potassium, rubidium, caesium; cadmium, mercury) to between 600 and 800 kJ mol$^{-1}$ (the heavy transition metals).

**Table 11**

| | m.p., $T/K$ | $\Delta H_{fusion}$ /(kJ mol$^{-1}$) at m.p. | $\Delta S_{fusion}$ /(J K$^{-1}$ mol$^{-1}$) at m.p. | b.p., $T/K$ | $\Delta H_{vap}$ /(kJ mol$^{-1}$) at b.p. | $\Delta S_{vap}$ /(J K$^{-1}$ mol$^{-1}$) at b.p. | $\Delta H_{atom}$ /(kJ mol$^{-1}$) (298 K) |
|---|---|---|---|---|---|---|---|
| Li | 453·7 | 3·01 | 6·6 | 1590 | 148 | 93 | 161 |
| Na | 371·0 | 2·60 | 7·0 | 1163 | 89 | 77 | 108 |
| K | 436·4 | 2·33 | 6·9 | 1037 | 77 | 75 | 90 |
| Rb | 311·9 | 2·20 | 7·1 | 974 | 69 | 71 | 82 |
| Cs | 301·8 | 2·18 | 7·2 | 958 | 66 | 69 | 78 |
| Be | 1556 | 12·5 | 8·0 | 2750 | 294 | 107 | 326 |
| Mg | 922·7 | 9·0 | 9·7 | 1390 | 132 | 95 | 149 |
| Ca | 1120 | 8·7 | 7·7 | 1760 | 150 | 85 | 177 |
| Sr | 1040 | 9·2 | 8·8 | 1640 | 139 | 85 | 164 |
| Ba | 980 | 7·7 | 7·8 | 1910 | 151 | 79 | 178 |
| Sc | 1670 | 16·1 | 9·6 | 3000 | 305 | 102 | 326 |
| Y | 1770 | 17·2 | 9·7 | 3500 | 393 | 113 | 410 |
| La | 1190 | 11·3 | 9·5 | 3640 | 400 | 110 | 435 |
| Ti | 1841 | 15·5 | 8·0 | 3550 | 430 | 121 | 473 |
| Zr | 2128 | 20·0 | 9·4 | 4650 | 582 | 125 | 611 |
| Hf | 2495 | 21·8 | 8·7 | 5500 | 661 | 121 | 703 |
| V | 2000 | 17·5 | 8·7 | 3650 | 458 | 125 | 515 |
| Nb | 2760 | 26·8 | 9·7 | 5200 | 696 | 134 | 774 |
| Ta | 3270 | 31·4 | 9·6 | 5700 | 753 | 133 | 781 |
| Cr | 2176 | 14·6 | 6·7 | 2915 | 349 | 120 | 397 |
| Mo | 2895 | 27·6 | 9·5 | 5100 | 594 | 117 | 659 |
| W | 3660 | 35·2 | 9·6 | 5800 | 799 | 138 | 837 |
| Mn | 1517 | 14·6 | 9·6 | 2368 | 225 | 95 | 281 |
| Tc | 2600 | 23 | 8·8 | 5000 | — | — | 649 |
| Re | 3450 | 38·0 | 11·0 | 5900 | 707 | 120 | 791 |
| Fe | 1808 | 15·9 | 8·8 | 3008 | 354 | 118 | 416 |
| Co | 1760 | 15·3 | 8·7 | 3150 | 383 | 121 | 425 |
| Ni | 1728 | 17·8 | 10·3 | 3100 | 380 | 124 | 430 |
| Ru | 2770 | 26 | 9·2 | 4380 | — | — | 669 |
| Rh | 2230 | 22 | 9·7 | 4230 | 531 | 126 | 577 |

Table 11—*continued*

| | m.p., $T/K$ | $\Delta H_{\text{fusion}}$ /(kJ mol$^{-1}$) at m.p. | $\Delta S_{\text{fusion}}$ /(J K$^{-1}$ mol$^{-1}$) at m.p. | b.p., $T/K$ | $\Delta H_{\text{vap}}$ /(kJ mol$^{-1}$) at b.p. | $\Delta S_{\text{vap}}$ /(J K$^{-1}$ mol$^{-1}$) at b.p. | $\Delta H_{\text{atom}}$ /(kJ mol$^{-1}$) (298 K) |
|----|------|-------|------|------|-----|-----|-----|
| Pd | 1828 | 17·2 | 9·4 | 3200 | — | — | 381 |
| Os | 2970 | 27 | 9·2 | 4700 | — | — | 728 |
| Ir | 2716 | 28 | 10·2 | 4620 | — | — | 690 |
| Pt | 2042 | 21·7 | 10·6 | 4100 | 447 | 108 | 566 |
| Cu | 1357 | 13·0 | 9·6 | 2868 | 304 | 106 | 339 |
| Ag | 1234·5 | 11·3 | 9·1 | 2485 | 254 | 102 | 286 |
| Au | 1338·0 | 12·8 | 9·5 | 3000 | 324 | 109 | 368 |
| Zn | 692·7 | 7·3 | 10·5 | 1180 | 115 | 97 | 125 |
| Cd | 594 | 6·4 | 10·8 | 1038 | 100 | 96 | 111 |
| Hg | 234·3 | 2·29 | 9·8 | 629·9 | 59 | 94 | 62 |
| Al | 931·8 | 10·7 | 11·5 | 2720 | 294 | 108 | 324 |
| Ga | 302·0 | 5·6 | 18·4 | 2500 | 254 | 102 | 272 |
| In | 429·4 | 13·27 | 7·6 | 2320 | 226 | 97 | 244 |
| Tl | 576·7 | 4·3 | 7·5 | 1730 | 162 | 94 | 180 |
| Ge | 1210·5 | 29·8 | 24·6 | 3100 | 334 | 108 | 372 |
| Sn | 505·1 | 7·1 | 14·0 | 2960 | 290 | 98 | 301 |
| Pb | 600·6 | 4·8 | 7·9 | 2024 | 179 | 89 | 197 |
| Bi | 544·5 | 10·9 | 20·0 | 1832 | 151 | 83 | 207 |
| Sb | 904·1 | 20·4 | 22·6 | — | — | — | 259 |

In contrast the entropies of vaporization for metals show a more restricted range of values: all but three of the metals listed in Table 11 have values of $\Delta S^{\circ}_{\text{b.p.}} = 105 \pm 30$ J K$^{-1}$ mol$^{-1}$. Because of this rough constancy of $\Delta S^{\circ}_{\text{b.p.}}$, there is a corresponding rough linearity between the boiling point and the heat of vaporization, as is evident from Figure 6. It is also clear from Table 11 that the heat of fusion at the melting point is very small compared to the heat of vaporization at the boiling point (numerically $\Delta H_{\text{fusion}}$ is seldom more than 5 per cent of $\Delta H^{\circ}_{\text{vap}}$); there is very little disruption of the metallic bonding when a metal crystal melts, and nearly all of the metallic bond strength is conserved until boiling occurs. Hence the approximate linearity of the boiling point–$\Delta H^{\circ}_{\text{vap}}$ plot referred to above and embodied in Figure 6 is preserved if $\Delta H^{\circ}_{\text{atom}}$ (298 K) is substituted for $\Delta H^{\circ}_{\text{vap}}$ (b.p.) (Figure 5), in spite of the fact that the two enthalpy quantities refer to different temperatures.

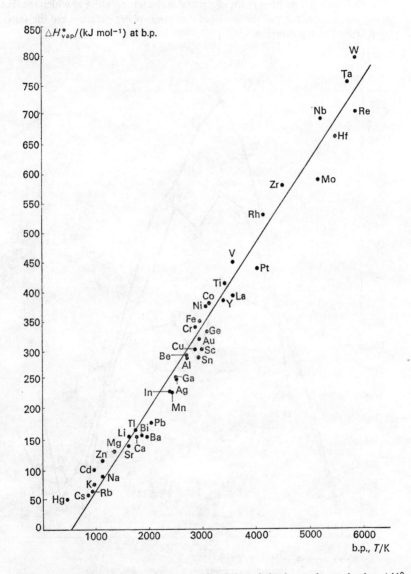

Figure 6   Relation between boiling point (K) and the heat of vaporization $\Delta H^{\circ}_{vap}$ of metals at the boiling point

**53   The Formation of Gaseous Atoms from Elements**

## 2.2.3  *Melting points of metals*

The conventional melting point of a metal is the temperature at which the free energies of the solid and the liquid at one atmosphere pressure are the same, that is for the equilibrium

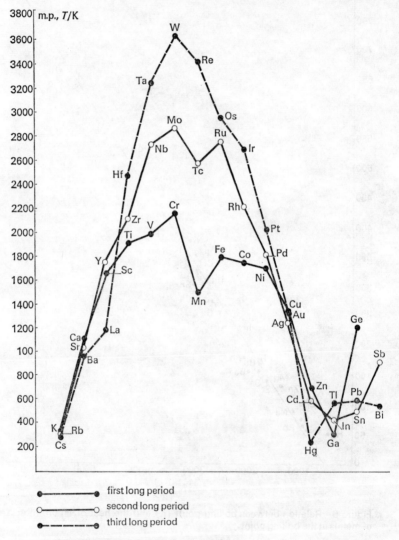

Figure 7   Melting points of metals (K)

$M(s) \rightleftharpoons M(l),$

$\Delta G^{\circ}_{m.p.} = 0$, and $\Delta H^{\circ}_{m.p.} = T \Delta S^{\circ}_{m.p.}$, where $T$ is the melting point in kelvins.

Hence $\quad T = \dfrac{\Delta H^{\circ}_{m.p.}}{\Delta S^{\circ}_{m.p.}},$

in other words the melting point (in kelvins) is the quotient of the heat of fusion and the entropy of fusion. Again, with a few noteworthy exceptions, the entropy of fusion (see Table 11) does not vary much; $\Delta S^{\circ}_{m.p.}$ for most metals is $8 \pm 2$ J $K^{-1}$ mol$^{-1}$, while the heats of fusion show a wider range of values, from about 2 kJ mol$^{-1}$ (potassium, rubidium, caesium) to as much as 30–40 kJ mol$^{-1}$ in the case of heavy transition metals such as tantalum, tungsten and rhenium. There are, however, several cases of metals with abnormally high entropies of fusion – in particular antimony (22·6 J $K^{-1}$ mol$^{-1}$), gallium (18·4), germanium (24·6), tin (14·0) and bismuth (20·0). Thus the very low melting point of gallium (302 K) is a consequence of the combination of a small heat of fusion (5·6 kJ mol$^{-1}$) and a particularly high entropy of fusion. In the periodic table, the melting points of the metals show the same broad general trends (Figure 7) as the boiling points, except that the metals following zinc, cadmium and mercury display very little regularity.

## 2.3 The formation of gaseous cations from gaseous atoms

A useful measure of the strength with which a gas-phase atom retains its electrons is provided by the energy required to remove them successively, that is the energy change for each of the stepwise processes

$M(g) - e \rightarrow M^+(g),$

$M^+(g) - e \rightarrow M^{2+}(g),$ etc.

The *ionization energy* of a gaseous atom or ion is the change in internal energy $\Delta U$ at 0 K which accompanies the ionization process; for example, the ionization energies of lithium are as follows:

$$\Delta U_0 / (\text{kJ mol}^{-1})$$

| | |
|---|---|
| $Li(g) - e \rightarrow Li^+(g)$ | 520 |
| $Li^+(g) - e \rightarrow Li^{2+}(g)$ | 7293 |
| $Li^{2+}(g) - e \rightarrow Li^{3+}(g)$ | 11 807 |

Energies such as these are commonly recorded in electron volts, and are then called *ionization potentials* (symbol $I$). An electron volt is the amount of energy acquired by an electron when it is accelerated through a potential difference of one volt. The conversion factors are

$$1 \text{ electron volt (eV) (per atom or ion)} = 96 \cdot 5 \text{ kJ mol}^{-1} = 23 \cdot 06 \text{ kcal mol}^{-1}.$$

For example, the *second* ionization potential of the species Li(g), which is identical with the *first* ionization potential of the species Li$^+$(g), is, from the data above, $\dfrac{7293}{96 \cdot 5} = 75 \cdot 6 \text{ eV}.$

Frequently ionization energies are encountered in energy cycles referring to constant-pressure conditions at 298 K, and it is then necessary to convert the quantity $\Delta U_0$ to $\Delta H_{298}$ in the following way:

For the process $M(g) \rightarrow M^+(g) + e(g)$,

$$\Delta H_{298} = \Delta U_0 + \int_0^{298} [C_p(M^+) + C_p(e) - C_p(M)] \, dT,$$

where $C_p$ is the heat capacity at constant pressure of the gaseous species shown in parenthesis, and $T$ is the absolute temperature.

If $M(g)$, $M^+(g)$, and $e(g)$ are all regarded as ideal monatomic gases, then, as discussed in section 1.3.2, their heat capacities may be taken as zero at 0 K, and equal to $\frac{5}{2}R$ at temperatures above 0 K, so that

$$\Delta H_{298} = \Delta U_0 + \int_0^{298} \tfrac{5}{2}R \, dT$$

$$= \Delta U_0 + \tfrac{5}{2}R(298).$$

Since at $T = 298 \text{ K}$, $\frac{5}{2}RT \approx 6 \cdot 2 \text{ kJ mol}^{-1}$, the correcting term is small and is often neglected in calculations unless a high degree of accuracy is required.

Ionization energies are collected in Table 12.

Table 12  Ionization Energies, $\Delta U_0/(\text{kJ mol}^{-1})$ (Ionization Potentials, $I/\text{eV}$)

|      | First | | Second | | Third | | Fourth | |
|------|-------|---|--------|---|-------|---|--------|---|
| 1 H  | 1311 | (13·595) | | | | | | |
| 2 He | 2372 | (24·580) | 5249 | (54·40) | | | | |
| 3 Li | 520·0 | (5·390) | 7297 | (75·62) | 11 810 | (122·42) | | |
| 4 Be | 899·1 | (9·320) | 1758 | (18·206) | 14 850 | (153·85) | 21 000 | (217·66) |
| 5 B  | 800·5 | (8·296) | 2428 | (25·15) | 2394 | (37·92) | 25 020 | (259·30) |
| 6 C  | 1086 | (11·256) | 2353 | (24·376) | 4618 | (47·87) | 6512 | (67·48) |

| | First | | Second | | Third | | Fourth | |
|---|---|---|---|---|---|---|---|---|
| 7 N | 1403 | (14·53) | 2855 | (29·59) | 4577 | (47·43) | 7473 | (77·45) |
| 8 O | 1410 | (13·61) | 3388 | (35·11) | 5297 | (54·89) | 7450 | (77·39) |
| 9 F | 1681 | (17·42) | 3375 | (34·98) | 6045 | (62·65) | 8409 | (87·14) |
| 10 Ne | 2080 | (21·559) | 3963 | (41·07) | 6130 | (63·5) | 9363 | (97·02) |
| 11 Na | 495·8 | (5·138) | 4561 | (57·29) | 6913 | (71·65) | 9543 | (98·88) |
| 12 Mg | 737·5 | (7·644) | 1450 | (15·03) | 7731 | (80·12) | 10 540 | (109·29) |
| 13 Al | 577·5 | (5·984) | 1817 | (18·82) | 2745 | (28·44) | 11 580 | (119·96) |
| 14 Si | 786·3 | (8·149) | 1577 | (16·34) | 3228 | (33·46) | 4355 | (45·13) |
| 15 P | 1012 | (10·484) | 1903 | (19·72) | 2910 | (30·156) | 4955 | (51·35) |
| 16 S | 999·3 | (10·357) | 2260 | (23·4) | 3380 | (35·0) | 4562 | (47·29) |
| 17 Cl | 1255 | (13·01) | 2297 | (23·80) | 3850 | (39·90) | 5160 | (53·5) |
| 18 Ar | 1520 | (15·755) | 2665 | (27·62) | 3950 | (40·90) | 5771 | (59·79) |
| 19 K | 418·7 | (4·339) | 3069 | (31·81) | 4400 | (46) | 5876 | (60·90) |
| 20 Ca | 589·6 | (6·111) | 1146 | (11·87) | 4942 | (51·21) | 6500 | (67) |
| 21 Sc | 631 | (6·54) | 1235 | (12·80) | 2389 | (24·75) | 7130 | (73·9) |
| 22 Ti | 656 | (6·82) | 1309 | (13·57) | 2650 | (27·47) | 4173 | (43·24) |
| 23 V | 650 | (6·74) | 1414 | (14·65) | 2828 | (29·31) | 4600 | (48) |
| 24 Cr | 652·5 | (6·763) | 1592 | (16·49) | 3056 | (30·95) | 4900 | (49·6) |
| 25 Mn | 717·1 | (7·432) | 1509 | (15·64) | 3251 | (33·69) | | |
| 26 Fe | 762 | (7·90) | 1561 | (16·18) | 2956 | (30·64) | | |
| 27 Co | 758 | (7·86) | 1644 | (17·05) | 3231 | (33·49) | | |
| 28 Ni | 736·5 | (7·633) | 1752 | (18·15) | 3489 | (36·16) | | |
| 29 Cu | 745·2 | (7·724) | 1958 | (20·29) | 3545 | (36·83) | | |
| 30 Zn | 906·1 | (9·391) | 1734 | (17·96) | 3831 | (39·70) | | |
| 31 Ga | 579 | (6·00) | 1979 | (20·51) | 2962 | (30·70) | 6190 | (64·2) |
| 32 Ge | 760 | (7·88) | 1537 | (15·93) | 3301 | (34·21) | 4410 | (45·7) |
| 33 As | 947 | (9·81) | 1798 | (18·63) | 2735 | (28·34) | 4830 | (50·1) |
| 34 Se | 941 | (9·75) | 2070 | (21·5) | 3090 | (32·0) | 4140 | (42·9) |
| 35 Br | 1142 | (11·84) | 2080 | (21·6) | 3460 | (35·9) | 4560 | (47·3) |
| 36 Kr | 1351 | (13·996) | 2370 | (24·56) | 3560 | (36·9) | | |
| 37 Rb | 402·9 | (4·176) | 2650 | (27·5) | 3900 | (40) | | |
| 38 Sr | 549·3 | (5·692) | 1064 | (11·03) | | | 5500 | (57) |
| 39 Y | 616 | (6·38) | 1180 | (12·23) | 1979 | (20·51) | | |
| 40 Zr | 674·1 | (6·984) | 1268 | (13·13) | 2217 | (22·98) | 3313 | (34·33) |
| 41 Nb | 664 | (6·88) | 1381 | (14·32) | 2416 | (25·04) | 3700 | (38·3) |
| 42 Mo | 685 | (7·10) | 1558 | (16·15) | 2618 | (27·13) | 4480 | (46·4) |
| 43 Tc | 703 | (7·28) | 1472 | (15·26) | 2850 | (29·54) | | |
| 44 Ru | 710·6 | (7·364) | 1617 | (16·76) | 2746 | (28·46) | | |
| 45 Rh | 720 | (7·46) | 1744 | (18·07) | 2996 | (31·05) | | |
| 46 Pd | 804 | (8·33) | 1874 | (19·42) | 3177 | (32·92) | | |
| 47 Ag | 730·8 | (7·574) | 2072 | (21·48) | 3360 | (34·82) | | |
| 48 Cd | 876·4 | (8·991) | 1630 | (16·90) | 3615 | (37·47) | | |
| 49 In | 558·1 | (5·785) | 1820 | (18·86) | 2705 | (28·03) | 5250 | (54·4) |
| 50 Sn | 708·2 | (7·342) | 1411 | (14·63) | 2942 | (30·49) | 3928 | (40·72) |
| 51 Sb | 833·5 | (8·639) | 1590 | (16·5) | 2440 | (25·3) | 4250 | (44·1) |
| 52 Te | 869 | (9·01) | 1800 | (18·6) | 3000 | (31) | 3600 | (38) |

**57   The Formation of Gaseous Cations from Gaseous Atoms**

**Table 12**—*continued*

| | *First* | | *Second* | | *Third* | | *Fourth* | |
|---|---|---|---|---|---|---|---|---|
| 53 I | 1191 | (10·454) | 1842 | (19·09) | | | | |
| 54 Xe | 1169 | (12·127) | 2050 | (21·2) | 3100 | (32·1) | | |
| 55 Cs | 375·5 | (3·893) | 2420 | (25·1) | | | | |
| 56 Ba | 502·5 | (5·210) | 964·8 | (10·001) | | | | |
| 57 La | 541 | (5·61) | 1103 | (11·43) | 1849 | (19·17) | | |
| 72 Hf | 760 | (7·9) | 1440 | (14·9) | 2250 | (23·3) | 3210 | (33·33) |
| 73 Ta | 760 | (7·88) | 1560 | (16·2) | | | | |
| 74 W | 770 | (7·98) | 1710 | (17·7) | | | | |
| 75 Re | 759 | (7·87) | 1600 | (16·6) | | | | |
| 76 Os | 840 | (8·7) | 1640 | (17·0) | | | | |
| 77 Ir | 900 | (9) | | | | | | |
| 78 Pt | 870 | (9·0) | 1791 | (18·56) | | | | |
| 79 Au | 889 | (9·22) | 1980 | (20·5) | | | | |
| 80 Hg | 1007 | (10·43) | 1809 | (18·751) | 3300 | (34·2) | | |
| 81 Tl | 588·9 | (6·106) | 1970 | (20·42) | 2880 | (29·8) | 4890 | (50·7) |
| 82 Pb | 715·3 | (7·415) | 1450 | (15·03) | 3080 | (31·93) | 4082 | (42·31) |
| 83 Bi | 702·9 | (7·287) | 1609 | (16·68) | 2465 | (25·56) | 4370 | (45·3) |
| 84 Po | 813 | (8·43) | | | | | | |
| 86 Rn | 1037 | (10·75) | | | | | | |
| 88 Ra | 509·1 | (5·277) | 978·6 | (10·144) | | | | |
| 89 Ac | 670 | (6·9) | 1170 | (12·1) | | | | |

Principal source of data: C. E. Moore (1949, 1952, 1958).

### 2.3.1 *Successive ionization energies (potentials)*

Successive ionization energies for the electrons of a given atom always increase in value, because each additional electron after the first is removed from a cation carrying an increasingly positive charge. For example, the ionization energies for the nine electrons of the fluorine atom F(g) increase from 1680 kJ mol$^{-1}$ for the first (F(g)$-$e $\rightarrow$ F$^+$(g)), to 106 300 kJ mol$^{-1}$ for the ninth (F$^{2+}$(g)$-$e$\rightarrow$F$^{2+}$(g)):

| | 1st | 2nd | 3rd | 4th | 5th | 6th | 7th | 8th | 9th |
|---|---|---|---|---|---|---|---|---|---|
| $\Delta U_0$ /(kJ mol$^{-1}$) | 1680 | 3380 | 6040 | 8400 | 11 000 | 15 200 | 17 800 | 92 000 | 106 300 |
| $I$/eV | 17·4 | 35·0 | 62·6 | 87·1 | 114 | 157 | 185 | 954 | 1102 |

The removal of an electron from a filled principal quantum level ($K$, $L$, $M$, etc., shell) is often evident from the sharp rise in ionization energy which accompanies the process. Several examples are shown in Figure 8. In the cases of boron B and fluorine F, the successive removal of the valence-shell ($2s$ and $2p$) electrons is followed by the rupture of the inner $1s$ shell and a dramatic rise in ionization energy. The rise is not quite so striking in the case of atoms like gallium Ga and mercury Hg, where the first inner-shell electron to be removed occupies a $3d$ (Ga) or $5d$ (Hg) orbital.

### 2.3.2  Variations in ionization energies (potentials) in the periodic system

The way in which the first ionization energy (potential) varies in the groups and rows of the periodic table is shown in Table 13.

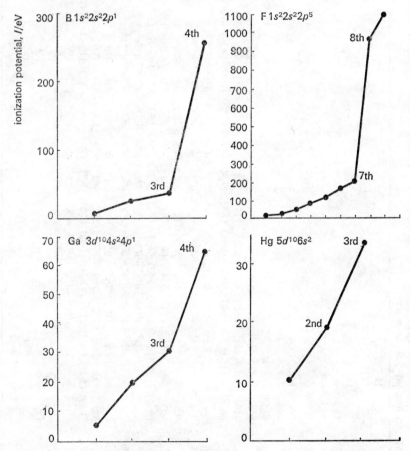

Figure 8   Successive ionization potentials (energies)

**Table 13** First Ionization Energies, $U_0$/(kJ mol$^{-1}$) (First Ionization Potentials, $I_1$/eV). The Ground-State Configuration of the Transition Metal Atoms (M) and Ions (M$^+$) are Shown

| 1 | 2 | 3 | 4 | 5 | 6 | 7 | 8 | 9 | 10 | 11 | 12 | 13 | 14 | 15 | 16 | 17 | 18 |
|---|---|---|---|---|---|---|---|---|---|---|---|---|---|---|---|---|---|
| H 1311 (13.59) | | | | | | | | | | | | | | | | | He 2372 (24.58) |
| Li 520 (5.39) | Be 899 (9.32) | | | | | | | | | | | B 801 (8.30) | C 1086 (11.26) | N 1403 (14.53) | O 1410 (13.61) | F 1681 (17.42) | Ne 2080 (21.56) |
| Na 496 (5.14) | Mg 737 (7.64) | | | | | | | | | | | Al 577 (5.98) | Si 786 (8.15) | P 1012 (10.48) | S 999 (10.36) | Cl 1255 (13.01) | Ar 1521 (15.76) |
| K 419 (4.34) | Ca 590 (6.11) | Sc 631 (6.54) | Ti 656 (6.82) | V 650 (6.74) | Cr 652 (6.76) | Mn 717 (7.43) | Fe 762 (7.90) | Co 758 (7.86) | Ni 736 (7.63) | Cu 745 (7.72) | Zn 906 (9.39) | Ga 579 (6.00) | Ge 760 (7.88) | As 947 (9.81) | Se 941 (9.75) | Br 1142 (11.84) | Kr 1351 (14.00) |
| Rb 403 (4.18) | Sr 549 (5.69) | Y 616 (6.38) | Zr 674 (6.98) | Nb 664 (6.88) | Mo 685 (7.10) | Tc 703 (7.28) | Ru 711 (7.36) | Rh 720 (7.46) | Pd 804 (8.33) | Ag 731 (7.57) | Cd 876 (8.99) | In 558 (5.79) | Sn 708 (7.34) | Sb 834 (8.64) | Te 869 (9.01) | I 1191 (10.54) | Xe 1169 (12.13) |
| Cs 375 (3.89) | Ba 503 (5.21) | La 541 (5.61) | Hf 760 (7.9) | Ta 760 (7.88) | W 770 (7.98) | Re 759 (7.87) | Os 840 (8.7) | Ir 900 (9) | Pt 870 (9.0) | Au 889 (9.22) | Hg 1007 (10.43) | Tl 589 (6.11) | Pb 715 (7.42) | Bi 703 (7.29) | Po 813 (8.43) | At | Rn 1037 (10.75) |
| Fr | Ra 509 (5.28) | Ac 670 (6.9) | | | | | | | | | | | | | | | |

Ground-state configurations of the transition metals:

M, $3d^a4s^b$ / M$^+$, $3d^a4s^b$:

| | Sc | Ti | V | Cr | Mn | Fe | Co | Ni | Cu | Zn |
|---|---|---|---|---|---|---|---|---|---|---|
| M | $d^1s^2$ | $d^2s^2$ | $d^3s^2$ | $d^5s^1$ | $d^5s^2$ | $d^6s^2$ | $d^7s^2$ | $d^8s^2$ | $d^9s^2$ | $d^{10}s^2$ |
| M$^+$ | $d^1s^1$ | $d^2s^1$ | $d^4s^0$ | $d^5s^0$ | $d^5s^1$ | $d^6s^1$ | $d^8s^0$ | $d^9s^0$ | $d^{10}s^0$ | $d^{10}s^1$ |

M, $4d^a5s^b$ / M$^+$, $4d^a5s^b$:

| | Y | Zr | Nb | Mo | Tc | Ru | Rh | Pd | Ag | Cd |
|---|---|---|---|---|---|---|---|---|---|---|
| M | $d^1s^2$ | $d^2s^2$ | $d^4s^1$ | $d^5s^1$ | $d^5s^2$ | $d^7s^1$ | $d^8s^1$ | $d^{10}s^0$ | $d^9s^2$ | $d^{10}s^2$ |
| M$^+$ | $d^0s^2$ | $d^2s^1$ | $d^4s^0$ | $d^5s^0$ | $d^5s^1$ | $d^7s^0$ | $d^8s^0$ | $d^9s^0$ | $d^{10}s^0$ | $d^{10}s^1$ |

M, $5d^a6s^b$ / M$^+$, $5d^a6s^b$:

| | La | Hf | Ta | W | Re | Os | Ir | Pt | Au | Hg |
|---|---|---|---|---|---|---|---|---|---|---|
| M | $d^1s^2$ | $d^2s^2$ | $d^3s^2$ | $d^4s^2$ | $d^5s^2$ | $d^6s^2$ | $d^7s^2$ | $d^9s^1$ | $d^{10}s^1$ | $d^{10}s^2$ |
| M$^+$ | $d^2s^0$ | $d^1s^2$ | $d^3s^1$ | $d^4s^1$ | $d^5s^1$ | $d^6s^1$ | ? | $d^9s^0$ | $d^{10}s^0$ | $d^{10}s^1$ |

The generalization is sometimes made that ionization energies (potentials) decrease from top to bottom down the groups, and increase from left to right across the periods; while this generalization holds in a broad general sense, deviations from it are so numerous that it is essential to study the groups and periods in more detail.

*Variations down groups.* The first ionization energy decreases monotonically down group 1 (the alkali metals); group 2 as far as barium; group 5 (nitrogen, phosphorus, arsenic, antimony, bismuth); group 6 (oxygen, sulphur, selenium, tellurium, polonium); group 7 (the halogens); and group 0 (the noble gases). The most marked departures from this general trend are observed in the groups of transition elements and in the groups immediately following them. Among the transition metals, the downward trend is observed for the group scandium, yttrium and lanthanum; for the other groups the trend is irregular, its most consistent feature being the very high ionization energies of the heaviest member of each group, that is of the metals of the third transition series. (See Figure 9). The cause of the high values for the series hafnium to mercury is undoubtedly the interpolation between element 57 (lanthanum) and element 72 (hafnium) of the lanthanide elements, in which the $4f$ subshell builds up from one to fourteen electrons. In the lanthanide sequence, the screening effect of each additional $4f$ electron is not sufficient to outweigh the attractive effect of each extra nuclear proton on the outer-shell electrons, so that a progressive decrease in radius ('lanthanide contraction') occurs. Hence element 72 (hafnium) differs from the group member immediately above it

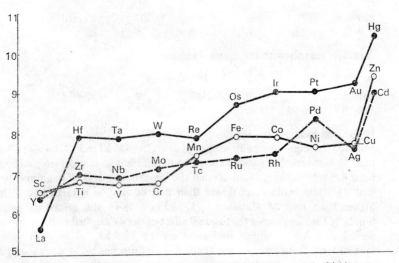

first ionization potential eV

Figure 9    First ionization potentials (energies) for transition metals, $I_1$/eV

**61    The Formation of Gaseous Cations from Gaseous Atoms**

(zirconium) in possessing a weakly screening inner $4f$ subshell and a correspondingly higher ionization energy (Hf = 760 kJ mol$^{-1}$; cf. Zr = 674 kJ mol$^{-1}$). The high value of the ionization energy is maintained along the third transition series and persists thereafter as far as lead (Pb).

The ionization energies of the members of the first and second transition series show many irregularities. After scandium, yttrium and lanthanum, the values for the members of the second transition series are at first higher than those of the first series, the order being titanium < zirconium < hafnium, vanadium < niobium < tantalum, chromium < molybdenum < tungsten; thereafter a reversal occurs, so that technetium < manganese < rhenium, ruthenium < iron < osmium, and rhodium < cobalt < iridium. There is then a reversion in the next group: nickel < palladium < platinum, and the series finishes with the orders silver < copper < gold and cadmium < zinc < mercury. The alternations in the relative values for the first and second transition series do not seem to arise from any easily identifiable cause, but it is noteworthy that there is very little consistency in each group in the ground-state configurations of either the neutral atoms or the unipositive cations. These configurations are shown in Table 13. For example, in the group vanadium, niobium and tantalum, the configurations of lowest energy in the neutral atoms are V = $d^3s^2$, Nb = $d^4s^1$, and Ta = $d^3s^2$, while those of the resulting singly charged ions are V$^+$ = $d^4s^0$, Nb$^+$ = $d^4s^0$, and Ta$^+$ = $d^3s^1$.

The presence of the three transition series has a noticeable effect on the elements which follow them in atomic number. The regularly decreasing sequence of ionization energies (potentials) in group 2, viz

| Be | Mg | Ca | Sr | Ba | |
|---|---|---|---|---|---|
| 899 | 737 | 590 | 549 | 503 | kJ mol$^{-1}$ |
| 9·32 | 7·64 | 6·11 | 5·69 | 5·21 | eV |

contrasts sharply with the group 3 sequence

| B | Al | Ga | In | Tl | |
|---|---|---|---|---|---|
| 801 | 577 | 579 | 558 | 589 | kJ mol$^{-1}$ |
| 8·30 | 5·98 | 6·00 | 5·79 | 6·11 | eV |

In the first long period, the poor shielding effect of the $3d$ electrons, responsible for the high ionization energy of zinc Zn (906 kJ mol$^{-1}$, cf. Ca, 590 kJ mol$^{-1}$), is substantially counteracted by the efficient screening provided by the filled $4s^2$ subshell in gallium, so that the ionization energy of gallium (579 kJ mol$^{-1}$), while being much lower than that of zinc, is nevertheless slightly higher than that of aluminium (577 kJ mol$^{-1}$) in the preceding period. Similarly thallium shows the residual effect of the $4f$ subshell in the third long period and has a higher ionization energy (589 kJ mol$^{-1}$) than indium (558 kJ mol$^{-1}$). In group 4 the $4f$ effect is still perceptible in lead, but in the succeeding groups the downward trend in ionization potential is consistent.

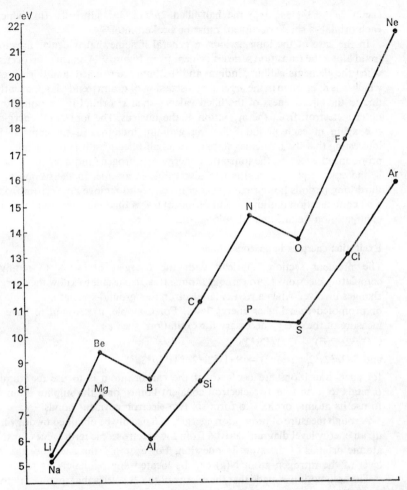

Figure 10  Ionization potentials (energies) of atoms of elements of the two short periods

*Variations across periods.* In a broad general way, the first ionization energy increases from left to right across each period; there are, however, a number of significant departures from the trend. The trends in the short periods lithium–neon and sodium–argon are shown in Figure 10. The general upward trend is unmistakable; the high values for beryllium and magnesium, and for nitrogen and phosphorus, can be attributed to the particular stability of filled or half-filled subshells. Thus in order to ionize beryllium ($1s^2 2s^2$) or magnesium ($1s^2 2s^2 2p^6 3s^2$) it is necessary to rupture the filled $2s^2$ (Be) or $3s^2$ (Mg) subshells, while in the case of nitrogen ($1s^2 2s^2 2p_x^1 2p_y^1 2p_z^1$) or phosphorus

**63   The Formation of Gaseous Atoms from Gaseous Ions**

$(1s^2 2s^2 2p^6 3s^2 3p_x^1\ 3p_y^1\ 3p_z^1)$ the half-filled $2p^3$ or $3p^3$ subshells (in which each orbital is singly occupied) must be broken into.

In the case of the long periods, a general if somewhat irregular upward trend along the transition series is evident from Figure 9. A sharp drop occurs when the elements gallium, indium and thallium are reached, and this effect, which was referred to in the preceding discussion of group trends, is apparently due to the effectiveness of the filled valence-shell $s^2$ orbital in screening the outer $p$-electron from the attraction of the nucleus. The ionization energies rise again in each period following gallium, indium and thallium; it is interesting that the particular stability of a half-filled $p^3$ subshell, which has a pronounced effect on the ionization energy of nitrogen (and a smaller effect in the case of phosphorus) is just discernible in arsenic. In the second and third long periods however the energy necessary to remove an electron from a $p^3$ configuration (antimony and bismuth) is less than that required for a $p^4$ configuration (tellurium and polonium).

## 2.4 Excitation energies in gaseous atoms

The previous section 2.3 dealt with the energies necessary to remove completely electrons from gaseous atoms. It is also useful to know the energy changes involved when a particular electron in a ground-state atom is excited or promoted to a higher energy level. For example, it is useful to have a measure of the energy necessary for excitations such as

C $(1s^2 2s^2 2p^2) \rightarrow$ C $(1s^2 2s^1 2p^3)$

and S $(1s^2 2s^2 2p^6 3s^2 3p^4) \rightarrow$ S $(1s^2 2s^2 2p^6 3s^1 3p^3 3d^2)$,

for such transitions are necessary if the carbon atom is to use its atomic orbitals to form four two-electron covalent bonds, or if the sulphur atom is to use its atomic orbitals to form six two-electron covalent bonds.

A rough measure of promotion energies can usually be obtained by drawing up an energy level diagram derived from the spectroscopic term values for the atomic orbitals of the atom in question. For example, the energy of the $2s$ level of the nitrogen atom N(g) can be located approximately as follows:

The assumption is made that the energy of the $2s$ level is that involved in the transition

N $(1s^2 2s^2 2p^3) \rightarrow$ N$^+(1s^2 2s^1 2p^3)$,

in which a $2s$ electron is removed completely from the ground-state atom. The required energy is then the sum of the energies involved in the transitions

N $(1s^2 2s^2 2p^3) \rightarrow$ N$^+$ $(1s^2 2s^2 2p^2)$         **2.1**

N$^+$ $(1s^2 2s^2 2p^2) \rightarrow$ N$^+$ $(1s^2 2s^1 2p^3)$.         **2.2**

There will in general be more than one spectroscopic state corresponding to the electron configurations shown above, that is, states differing in the total spin quantum number $S$, the orbital angular momentum quantum number $L$ and the total angular momentum quantum number $J$, and the arbitrary convention is adopted of choosing the state of lowest energy. The energy of transition **2.1** above is then the normal ionization energy of N(g), viz 1403 kJ mol$^{-1}$. The energy transition **2.2**, derived from spectroscopic tables for the species N$^+$(g), is 4 716 800 m$^{-1}$ which is equivalent to 564 kJ mol$^{-1}$ when converted by use of the conversion factor 1 kJ mol$^{-1}$ = 8358 m$^{-1}$. The energy of the transition

$$N\ (1s^2 2s^2 2p^3) \rightarrow N^+\ (1s^2 2s^1 2p^3)$$

is thus   1403 + 564 = 1967 kJ mol$^{-1}$.

By this sort of procedure, the data shown in Table 14 and plotted in Figure 11 for the elements of the first two short periods were obtained. It must be

**Table 14**   Energies/(kJ mol$^{-1}$) of Atomic Orbitals in Gaseous Atoms (Figures in Parentheses are Energies/eV)

|     | Li          | Be          | B            | C            |
| --- | ----------- | ----------- | ------------ | ------------ |
| $4s$ |             |             |              |              |
| $3d$ |             |             | 145  (1·50)  | 157   (1·63) |
| $3p$ |             |             |              | 262   (2·72) |
| $3s$ | 195  (2·02) | 277  (2·87) | 322  (3·77)  | 355   (3·77) |
| $2p$ | 342  (3·54) | 637  (6·60) | 801  (8·30)  | 1090 (11·3)  |
| $2s$ | 520  (5·39) | 899  (9·32) | 1250 (12·9)  | 1600 (16·6)  |

|     | N           | O            | F            |     |
| --- | ----------- | ------------ | ------------ | --- |
| $4s$ |             |              |              |     |
| $3d$ | 147  (1·52) | 148  (1·53)  | 117  (1·21)  |     |
| $3p$ | 282  (2·93) | 277  (2·87)  | 294  (3·05)  |     |
| $3s$ | 407  (4·22) | 431  (4·47)  | 456  (4·73)  |     |
| $2p$ | 1400 (14·5) | 1310 (13·6)  | 1680 (17·4)  |     |
| $2s$ | 1970 (20·4) | 2740 (28·4)  | 3650 (37·8)  |     |

|     | Na          | Mg           | Al           | Si           |
| --- | ----------- | ------------ | ------------ | ------------ |
| $4s$ | 188  (1·95) | 245  (2·54)  | 274  (2·84)  | 312  (3·23)  |
| $3d$ | 147  (1·52) | 182  (1·89)  | 189  (1·96)  | 245  (2·54)  |
| $3p$ | 293  (3·04) | 477  (4·94)  | 577  (5·98)  | 787  (8·15)  |
| $3s$ | 496  (5·14) | 737  (7·64)  | 1020 (10·6)  | 1310 (13·6)  |
| $2p$ | 3670 (38·0) | 4810 (49·8)  | 7030 (72·9)  | 9460 (98)    |

|     | P             | S             | Cl            |     |
| --- | ------------- | ------------- | ------------- | --- |
| $4s$ | 311   (3·22)  | 370   (3·83)  | 395   (4·09)  |     |
| $3d$ | 169   (1·75)  | 187   (1·94)  |               |     |
| $3p$ | 1011  (10·48) | 1000  (10·4)  | 1250  (13·0)  |     |
| $3s$ | 1639  (16·98) | 1950  (20·2)  | 2370  (24·6)  |     |
| $2p$ | 12 400 (128)  | 15 600 (162)  | 19 400 (201)  |     |

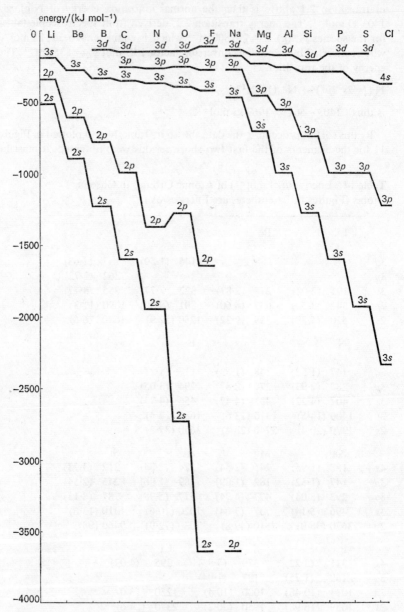

energy/(kJ mol⁻¹)

Figure 11   Energies of atomic orbitals in gaseous atoms

emphasized that these energies are the result of crude approximations applied to gas-phase atoms and ions. Their status will be discussed again when valence-state energies are considered in section 4.2. At this stage only a typical example of their use will be quoted.

It is well known that certain compounds formed by second row atoms, such as $K_2SiF_6$, $PF_5$ and $SF_6$, have no analogues in the case of the corresponding first row atoms – there is no $K_2CF_6$, $NF_5$ or $OF_6$. The conventional explanation of this phenomenon is that the species $SiF_6^{2-}$, $PF_5$ and $SF_6$, when formulated with two-electron covalent bonds, require the accommodation of more than eight electrons in the central atom's valence orbitals; this can only be achieved by the use of $3d$ orbitals by the atoms concerned, which are said to 'expand the octet'. The first row atoms, however, never form stable compounds in which there are more than eight electrons in the valence orbitals, and it is usually argued that the use of $3d$ orbitals by first row atoms (there are of course no $2d$ orbitals) is precluded by the excessively high excitation energies necessary to bring them into use. The $2s \rightarrow 3d$ excitation energies for some first row atoms, and the $3s \rightarrow 3d$ excitation energies for the second row analogues are, from the data of Table 14 as follows:

|  | B | C | N | O | F |  |
|---|---|---|---|---|---|---|
| $2s \rightarrow 3d$ | 1100 | 1443 | 1822 | 2592 | 3530 | kJ mol$^{-1}$ |
|  | 11·4 | 14·97 | 18·88 | 26·87 | 36·59 | eV |

|  | Al | Si | P | S |  |
|---|---|---|---|---|---|
| $3s \rightarrow 3d$ | 830 | 1070 | 1470 | 1760 | kJ mol$^{-1}$ |
|  | 8·64 | 11·14 | 15·25 | 18·26 | eV |

Clearly the excitation energies for the first row elements are much higher than those for the corresponding second row elements; nevertheless, the excitation energies for some of the second row elements – notably phosphorus and sulphur – are as high as those of boron, carbon and nitrogen. There would therefore appear to be some doubt as to either the use of $3d$ orbitals even by second row atoms, or the reliability of the values of the excitation energies quoted as a guide to the feasibility of the participation of $3d$ orbitals in bonding.

## 2.5 The formation of gaseous anions from gaseous atoms; electron affinities

The change in internal energy at 0 K, $\Delta U_0$, which accompanies the addition of an electron to an atom to form a negative ion in the gas phase,

i.e. $X(g) + e \rightarrow X^-(g)$

is called the *electron affinity* of the atom. Direct experimental determinations of electron affinities have been achieved in relatively few cases. As is the case for ionization energies, electron affinities are often encountered in enthalpy cycles referring to 298 K, and the conversion of $\Delta U_0$ to $\Delta H_{298}$ can be made as follows:

For the process $X(g) + e \rightarrow X^-(g)$,

$$\Delta H_{298} = \Delta U_0 + \int_0^{298} [C_p(X^-) - C_p(X) - C_p(e)]\, dT.$$

If it is assumed that $C_p$ for the gaseous species X, X$^-$, and e is equal to zero at 0 K and to $\frac{5}{2}R$ or $20\cdot8$ J K$^{-1}$ mol$^{-1}$ at other temperatures, then

$$\Delta H_{298} = \Delta U_0 - \tfrac{5}{2}RT,$$

which with $T = 298\cdot2$ K gives

$$\Delta H_{298} = \Delta U_0 - 6\cdot2 \text{ kJ mol}^{-1}.$$

In certain enthalpy cycles referring to 298 K, both an ionization potential and an electron affinity sometimes contribute; if the number of electrons involved in each term is the same, then the correcting terms $\frac{5}{2}RT$ cancel out and $\Delta U_0$ values may be used without adjustment.

**Table 15**  Electron Affinities, $-\Delta U_0^\circ/(\text{kJ mol}^{-1})$ ($E/\text{eV}$), for the Process $X(g) + e \rightarrow X^+(g)$

| | | | | | | | |
|---|---|---|---|---|---|---|---|
| H | | | | | | | He |
| 72 | | | | | | | $-54$ |
| (0·75) | | | | | | | ($-0$·56) |
| Li | Be | B | C | N | O | F | Ne |
| 57 | $-66$ | 15 | 121 | $-31$ | 142 | 333 | $-99$ |
| (0·59) | ($-0$·68) | (0·16) | (1·25) | ($-0$·32) | (1·47) | (3·45) | ($-1$·03) |
| Na | Mg | Al | Si | P | S | Cl | |
| 21 | $-67$ | 26 | 135 | 60 | 200 | 348 | |
| (0·22) | ($-0$·69) | (0·27) | (1·40) | (0·62) | (2·07) | (3·61) | |
| | | | | | | Br | |
| | | | | | | 324 | |
| | | | | | | (3·36) | |
| | | | | | | I | |
| | | | | | | 295 | |
| | | | | | | (3·06) | |
| | | | | | | At* | |
| | | | | | | 256 | |
| | | | | | | (2·69) | |

Principal source of data: R. J. S. Crossley (1964).
*M. F. C. Ladd and W. H. Lee (1961).

Some electron affinities are collected in Table 15, and are listed as values of $-\Delta U_0^\circ$ for the process $X(g) + e \rightarrow X^-(g)$. The data are taken mainly from the compilation of R. J. S. Crossley (1964); some of the values are experimental, while others are the result of extrapolation procedures. In several cases (beryllium, magnesium, nitrogen, helium, neon) the addition of an electron to the gaseous atom is an energy-absorbing process. Two-electron affinities are known in a few cases, e.g.

| | $-\Delta U_0^\circ/(kJ\ mol^{-1})$ | $-E/eV$ |
|---|---|---|
| $O(g) + e \rightarrow O^-(g)$ | 142 | 1·47 |
| $O^-(g) + e \rightarrow O^{2-}(g)$ | −844 | −8·75 |
| $O(g) + 2e \rightarrow O^{2-}(g)$ | −702 | −7·28 |
| $S(g) + e \rightarrow S^-(g)$ | 200 | 2·07 |
| $S^-(g) + e \rightarrow S^{2-}(g)$ | −532 | −5·51 |
| $S(g) + 2e \rightarrow S^{2-}(g)$ | −332 | −3·44 |

Thus while the addition of an electron to the neutral atoms O and S releases energy, the addition of a second electron to the ions $O^-$ and $S^-$, which are already negatively charged, is accompanied by quite a high energy absorption.

# Chapter 3
# Energetics of Ionic Crystals

## 3.1 General

The term 'ionic crystal' is conventionally applied to those substances (of which sodium chloride is the prototype) whose structures can be conveniently represented as regular crystalline arrays of oppositely charged ions. Such a representation is of course no more than a convenient conceptual model, for it is widely recognized that in general the bonding in such crystals involves a proportion of covalent character – a proportion which will be minimal in crystals represented as being composed of singly-charged ions derived from elements of widely differing electronegatives (such as $Cs^+F^-$), and substantial in crystals represented as being composed of cations which are small and highly charged, and anions which are large and highly charged. The convenience of the ionic model lies in its allowing the application of relatively simple electrostatic arguments for the calculation of binding energies. For example, as will be seen in the course of this chapter, ionic-model calculations of binding energies for the alkali metal halide crystals yield results which are 98–99 per cent of the experimental values. For crystals such as CuBr and AgI, however, only about 90 per cent of the binding energy can be accounted for by such calculations. While it may be justifiable in the latter cases to attribute the discrepancy to 'covalent contributions' in a qualitative sort of way, it is dangerous to infer that the extent of such contributions can be measured by the difference between the experimental and calculated results. There is no simple and straightforward theoretical technique for incorporating partly covalent interactions; unfortunately the absence of such a technique provides the principal justification for the widespread adoption of an ionic model in cases where its application to the structure under consideration is of marginal validity.

## 3.2 Lattice energy

The lattice energy $U$ of a crystal is the energy liberated when one mole of the substance is formed from its constituent gas-phase ions. For example, for sodium chloride NaCl the lattice energy is the change in internal energy $\Delta U_0$ which accompanies the process

$$Na^+(g) + Cl^-(g) \rightarrow NaCl(s)$$

at 0 K.

Sometimes the lattice energy is defined as the energy absorbed in the reverse process (i.e. the dissociation of the crystal into gaseous ions), in which case the sign of the lattice energy is positive.

These processes often occur as steps in enthalpy cycles referring to constant-pressure conditions at 298 K. In such circumstances the relevant energy quantity is not $\Delta U_0$ but the lattice enthalpy $\Delta H_{298}$; in the case of sodium chloride the two quantities are related as follows:

$$\Delta H_{298} = \Delta U_0 + \int_0^{298} [C_p(NaCl) - C_p(Na^+) - C_p(Cl^-)]\, dT,$$

where $C_p$ is the constant-pressure heat capacity (see section 1.3.2) and $T$ is the absolute temperature.

For rough calculations it is often assumed that the lattice energy $\Delta U$ does not alter much with temperature, that is in the relationship

$$\Delta H_{298} = \Delta U_{298} + P\,\Delta V,$$

$\Delta U_0$ is assumed equal to $\Delta U_{298}$, and since, for NaCl, $P\,\Delta V = -2RT$,

$$\Delta H_{298} \approx \Delta U_0 - 2RT.$$

A further approximation can be introduced by ignoring the small contribution $2RT$ (about $5\,kJ\,mol^{-1}$ at 298 K), so that in room-temperature enthalpy cycles of a relatively low order of accuracy $\Delta U_0$ may be used without correction.

There is no satisfactory experimental method for measuring lattice energies *directly*, and 'experimental' lattice energies are those deduced from heats of formation by use of suitable energy cycles, commonly called 'Born–Haber' cycles.

Example: NaCl. $\Delta H_f^\circ = -411\,kJ\,mol^{-1}$,

that is, for the reaction

$$Na(s) + \tfrac{1}{2}Cl_2(g) \to NaCl(s) \qquad \Delta H_{298}^\circ = -411\,kJ\,mol^{-1}.$$

This reaction can be represented as the resultant of the following steps.

|       |                                        |            | Sign |
|-------|----------------------------------------|------------|------|
| (i)   | $Na(s) \to Na(g)$                      | $\Delta h_1$ | +    |
| (ii)  | $Na(g) \to Na^+(g) + e$                | $\Delta h_2$ | +    |
| (iii) | $\tfrac{1}{2}Cl_2(g) \to Cl(g)$        | $\Delta h_3$ | +    |
| (iv)  | $Cl(g) + e \to Cl^-(g)$                | $\Delta h_4$ | −    |
| (v)   | $Na^+(g) + Cl^-(g) \to NaCl(s)$        | $\Delta h_5$ | −    |
|       | $Na(s) + \tfrac{1}{2}Cl_2(g) \to NaCl(s)$ | $\Delta H$ | −    |

$\Delta h_2$ can be evaluated from the experimental ionization energy of Na(g),

$$Na(g) \rightarrow Na^+(g) + e \qquad \Delta U_0 = 495{\cdot}8 \text{ kJ mol}^{-1},$$

whence $\Delta h_2 = 502 \text{ kJ mol}^{-1}$ (see section 2.3).

$\Delta h_4$ is obtained from the electron affinity of $Cl(g)$, viz $348 \text{ kJ mol}^{-1}$, whence $\Delta h_4 = -354 \text{ kJ mol}^{-1}$ (see section 2.5).

$\Delta h_1$ and $\Delta h_3$ are obtained from the heats of atomization of the elements (see section 2.2),

$$\Delta h_1 = 108 \text{ kJ mol}^{-1}$$

and $\quad \Delta h_3 = 121 \text{ kJ mol}^{-1}$

$$
\begin{aligned}
\text{hence} \quad \Delta h_5 &= \Delta H - (\Delta h_1 + \Delta h_2 + \Delta h_3 + \Delta h_4) \\
&= -411 - (108 + 502 + 121 - 354) \\
&= -788 \text{ kJ mol}^{-1} = \text{the lattice enthalpy, } \Delta H^\circ_{298}.
\end{aligned}
$$

This corresponds to a lattice energy $\Delta U_{298}$ of $-782 \text{ kJ mol}^{-1}$.

### 3.3 Calculation of lattice energies

#### 3.3.1 *Simple expressions*

The simplest expressions for the calculation of lattice energies are obtained by regarding the crystal as an assemblage of spherical ions (i.e. by adopting a purely ionic model) and by evaluating (a) the energy of the attractive (energy-lowering) Coulomb forces between the oppositely charged ions, and (b) the repulsive (energy-increasing) Born forces resulting from the interpenetration of the spherical charge clouds of the ions.

*The Coulomb attraction* $U_C$. The potential energy of a pair of oppositely charged ions $M^+$ and $X^-$ brought from infinity to a distance $r$ between their nuclei is

$$-\frac{e^2}{4\pi\varepsilon_0 \, r},$$

where $e$ is the unit of electrical charge and $\varepsilon_0 = 8{\cdot}854 \times 10^{-12} \text{ F m}^{-1}$. For a mole of such ion pairs, the energy is

$$-\frac{N_A e^2}{4\pi\varepsilon_0 \, r},$$

where $N_A$ is Avogadro's constant. For a mole of $M^+X^-$ units *in a crystal lattice*, the energy must be multiplied by a constant which allows for the fact that in ionic crystals the Coulomb forces are not restricted to inter-actions between pairs of ions. For example in the sodium chloride crystal each of the ions $Na^+$ and $Cl^-$ is surrounded by six octahedrally arranged oppositely charged ions at a distance $r$; by twelve ions of the same charge at a distance $\sqrt{2}r$; by eight oppositely charged ions at a distance $\sqrt{3}r$; by six of the same charge at a distance $2r$, and so on.

Thus (the potential energy) $= -6\dfrac{e^2}{4\pi\varepsilon_0\,r} + 12\dfrac{e^2}{4\pi\varepsilon_0\,\sqrt{2}r} - 8\dfrac{e^2}{4\pi\varepsilon_0\,\sqrt{3}r} +$

$$+6\dfrac{e^2}{4\pi\varepsilon_0\,2r} - \cdots$$

$$= -\dfrac{e^2}{4\pi\varepsilon_0\,r}\left(6 - 12\dfrac{1}{\sqrt{2}} + 8\dfrac{1}{\sqrt{3}} - 6\dfrac{1}{2} + \cdots\right).$$

The series in brackets can be summed by mathematical methods and yields a constant (called the Madelung constant, $A$) whose value depends solely on the geometry of the crystal; for example, for crystals with the sodium chloride structure, $A = 1\cdot74756$.

Hence the Coulomb energy of a mole of ions $M^+X^-$ in a sodium chloride lattice is

$$U_C = -\dfrac{N_A A e^2}{4\pi\varepsilon_0\,r}.$$

The Madelung constants for a number of common crystal types are listed in Table 16.

**Table 16**   Madelung Constants

| Structure | $A$ |
|---|---|
| sodium chloride (NaCl) | 1·74756 |
| caesium chloride (CsCl) | 1·76267 |
| zinc blende (ZnS) | 1·63806 |
| würtzite (ZnS) | 1·64132 |
| calcium fluoride (CaF$_2$) | 5·03878 |
| rutile (TiO$_2$) | 4·816 |
| cadmium iodide (CdI$_2$) | 4·71 |
| $\beta$-quartz (SiO$_2$) | 4·4394 |

The general expression for the Coulomb energy of an ionic crystal is

$$U_C = -\dfrac{N_A\,A z^2 e^2}{4\pi\varepsilon_0\,r},$$

in which $z$ is the highest common factor of the numerical values of the charges on the ions. Examples: for $Na^+Cl^-$ and $Ca^{2+}2F^-$, $z = 1$; for $Ca^{2+}O^{2-}$ and $Ti^{4+}2O^{2-}$, $z = 2$.

Thus for NaCl, $N_A = 6\cdot023 \times 10^{23}$ mol$^{-1}$, $A = 1\cdot748$, $e = 1\cdot602 \times 10^{-19}$ C, $z = 1$ and $r = 2\cdot814 \times 10^{-10}$ m.

Thus
$$U_C = -\frac{6 \cdot 023 \times 10^{23} \times 1 \cdot 748 \times 1 \times (1 \cdot 602 \times 10^{-19})^2}{4 \times 3 \cdot 142 \times 8 \cdot 854 \times 10^{-12} \times 2 \cdot 814 \times 10^{-10}} \text{ J mol}^{-1}$$

$$= -8 \cdot 63 \times 10^5 \text{ J mol}^{-1}$$

$$= -863 \text{ kJ mol}^{-1}.$$

This is the Coulomb energy liberated when the process

$$Na^+(g) + Cl^-(g) \rightarrow NaCl(s)$$

occurs at 0 K. For the reverse process the sign of $U_C$ is of course positive.

*The Born repulsion* $U_B$. In crystals there is a characteristic repulsive force between the ions due to the interpenetration or overlap of their electron clouds; it was assumed by Born and Landé to be proportional to $r^{-n}$,

i.e. $$U_B = \frac{N_A B}{r^n},$$

where $N_A$ is the Avogadro constant, $B$ is a proportionality constant and $n$ is the 'Born exponent'.

The value of the Born exponent $n$ is determined experimentally from the compressibility of the crystal; the following are rounded average values found for crystals of various ion-types:

| Ion-type | Example | n |
|---|---|---|
| He–He | LiH | 5 |
| Ne–Ne | MgO, NaF | 7 |
| (Ar or Cu$^+$)–Ar | KCl, CuCl | 9 |
| (Kr or Ag$^+$)–Kr | RbBr, AgBr | 10 |
| (Xe or Au$^+$)–Xe | CsI | 12 |

For mixed ion-types, the appropriate average is used,

e.g. Li$^+$Cl$^-$ (He–Ar), $n = \frac{1}{2}(5+9) = 7$.

The resultant of the attractive (Coulomb) and repulsive (Born) terms is thus

$$U_{C+B} = -\frac{N_A A z^2 e^2}{4\pi\varepsilon_0 r} + \frac{N_A B}{r^n}.$$

The constant $B$ can be eliminated by using the fact that at the equilibrium distance ($r = r_0$) the attractive and repulsive forces are balanced, so that

$$\left(\frac{dU}{dr}\right)_{r=r_0} = 0 = \frac{N_A\, Az^2e^2}{4\pi\varepsilon_0\, r_0^2} - \frac{nN_A\, B}{r_0^{n+1}}$$

and $B = \dfrac{Az^2e^2 r_0^{n-1}}{4\pi\varepsilon_0\, n}$.

Hence $U_{C+B} = -\dfrac{N_A\, Az^2e^2}{4\pi\varepsilon_0\, r_0} + \dfrac{N_A\, Az^2e^2}{4\pi\varepsilon_0\, nr_0}$

$$= -\frac{N_A\, Az^2e^2}{4\pi\varepsilon_0\, r_0}\left(1 - \frac{1}{n}\right).$$

This is the simple *Born–Landé* expression for the lattice energy. As an example, for sodium chloride, $n = 8$ and $\left(1 - \dfrac{1}{n}\right) = \dfrac{7}{8}$, thus the repulsive (Born) energy is equal and opposite in sign to $\frac{1}{8}$ of the attractive Coulomb energy.

Since $U_C = -863\ \text{kJ mol}^{-1}$ at 0 K,

$U_B = \frac{1}{8} \times 863 = 108\ \text{kJ mol}^{-1}$ at 0 K.

Hence $U_{C+B} = -863 + 108 = -755\ \text{kJ mol}^{-1}$ at 0 K.

Born and Mayer used a different expression for the repulsive energy $U_B$. Because the electron density of a spherically symmetrical ion falls off exponentially at its periphery, the repulsive energy should be proportional to $\exp(-r/\rho)$,

i.e. $U_B = B \exp\left(-\dfrac{r}{\rho}\right)$,

where $B$ is again a proportionality constant, $r$ is the internuclear distance, and $\rho$ is a constant, taken for many crystals to be $0.345 \times 10^{-10}$ m.

Hence according to Born and Mayer,

$$U_{C+B} = -\frac{N_A\, Az^2e^2}{4\pi\varepsilon_0\, r} + B \exp\left(-\frac{r}{\rho}\right).$$

The constant $B$ can be eliminated as before by making use of the fact that when $r = r_0$, $\dfrac{dU}{dr} = 0$,

so that $U_{C+B} = -\dfrac{N_A\, Az^2e^2}{4\pi\varepsilon_0\, r_0}\left(1 - \dfrac{\rho}{r_0}\right).$

This is the simple *Born–Mayer* expression for the lattice energy.

For sodium chloride, where $r_0 = 2 \cdot 814 \times 10^{-10}$ m,

$$\frac{\rho}{r_0} = \frac{0 \cdot 345 \times 10^{-10}}{2 \cdot 814 \times 10^{-10}}$$

$$= 0 \cdot 1226,$$

which gives a repulsive energy $U_B$ of $863 \times 0 \cdot 1226 = 106$ kJ mol$^{-1}$ at 0 K, which in this case differs only slightly from the value (108 kJ mol$^{-1}$) obtained from the Born–Landé expression.

### 3.3.2 Extended expressions

The simple Born–Landé and Born–Mayer expressions for the lattice energy do not explicitly take into account the contributions of the attractive London (dispersion or van der Waals) forces which exist between all the ions in a crystal. To incorporate the London energy $U_L$, it is necessary to add further terms to the simple expressions described above.

*The London energy $U_L$.* For spherical ions, the London energy involves two terms: the first arises from the dipole–dipole component of the dispersion forces, and the associated energy is proportional to $r^{-6}$; the second arises from the dipole–quadrupole component, and the associated energy is proportional to $r^{-8}$. Hence the lattice energy can be represented by the sum

$$U = -\frac{N_A A z^2 e^2}{4\pi\varepsilon_0 r} + N_A B \exp\left(-\frac{r}{\rho}\right) - N_A \frac{C}{r^6} - N_A \frac{D}{r^8},$$

where $C$ and $D$ are new proportionality constants.

If all the terms are minimized at the equilibrium distance $r = r_0$, the relationship

$$U = N_A \left\{ -\frac{A z^2 e^2}{4\pi\varepsilon_0 r_0}\left(1 - \frac{\rho}{r_0}\right) - \frac{C}{r_0^6}\left(1 - \frac{6\rho}{r_0}\right) - \frac{D}{r_0^8}\left(1 - \frac{8\rho}{r_0}\right) \right\}$$

is obtained, in which $\rho$, as before, is determined from the crystal compressibility and has values close to $0 \cdot 345 \times 10^{-10}$ m for crystals with the sodium chloride structure.

Unfortunately the evaluation of the constants $C$ and $D$ is a complicated matter. The term involving $D$ is small enough to be neglected in an approximate treatment.

The procedure for the evaluation of the constant $C$ and of the dipole–dipole London energy $\frac{C}{r^6}$, is as follows:

For a *pair* of ions M$^+$X$^-$,

$$C_{\text{ion-pair}} = \frac{3}{2} \frac{E_1 E_2}{(E_1 + E_2)} \alpha_1 \alpha_2,$$

where $\alpha_1$ and $\alpha_2$ are the polarizabilities, and $E_1$ and $E_2$ are characteristic energies of the two ions $M^+$ and $X^-$. The characteristic energy $E$ of an ion is theoretically the quantity $h\nu$, where $\nu$ is the main ultraviolet absorption frequency of the ion in the crystal. In practice, approximations may be used for these energies, and the case of silver chloride is described below. If the ions constitute a crystal lattice of stoichiometry MX, the interactions must of course be summed for the positive ion–negative ion $(C_{+-})$, positive ion–positive ion $(C_{++})$ and negative ion–negative ion $(C_{--})$ attractions, so that

$$C_{+-} = \frac{3}{2} \frac{E_+ E_-}{(E_+ + E_-)} \alpha_+ \alpha_-,$$

$$C_{++} = \tfrac{3}{4} E_+ \alpha_+^2,$$

$$C_{--} = \tfrac{3}{4} E_- \alpha_-^2$$

and $\quad C_{\text{crystal}} = kC_{+-} + k'\tfrac{1}{2}(C_{++} + C_{--}),$

where $k$ and $k'$ are summation constants whose values depend on the type of crystal lattice – see Table 17.

**Table 17** Summation Constants
(J. Lennard-Jones and A. E. Ingham, 1925)

| Type of lattice | Coordination | $k$ | $k'$ |
|---|---|---|---|
| NaCl | 6 : 6 | 6·595 | 1·807 |
| CsCl | 8 : 8 | 8·709 | 3·545 |
| ZnS | 4 : 4 | 4·354 | 0·762 |

It is therefore possible to evaluate $C$, and thence the dipole–dipole energy $\dfrac{C}{r^6}$, provided that, in addition to the internuclear distance $r$, the polarizabilities $\alpha_+$ and $\alpha_-$ of the ions and their characteristic energies $E_+$ and $E_-$ are known.

The selection of appropriate values of the polarizabilities and energies is a complex matter which does not easily lend itself to simple generalization. The following calculation of the dispersion energy for silver chloride illustrates the procedure used by J. E. Mayer (1933):

AgCl (NaCl structure)   $r_0 = 2·772 \times 10^{-10}$ m.

Polarizabilities:

For the positive ion $Ag^+$, $\alpha_+$ was assigned the value calculated by Pauling from the mole refraction, viz

$$\alpha_{Ag^+} = 1 \cdot 72 \times 10^{-30} \, m^3.$$

Pauling's values for the polarizabilities of a number of ions are listed in Table 18.

**Table 18**  Polarizabilities, $\alpha/(10^{-30} \, m^3)$
Calculated from mole refractions ($R_0$); see L. Pauling (1927).

| $\alpha_+$ | | | | |
|---|---|---|---|---|
| $Li^+$ | $Be^{2+}$ | $Cu^+$ | $Zn^{2+}$ | $Al^{3+}$ |
| 0·029 | 0·008 | 0·43 | 0·29 | 0·054 |
| $Na^+$ | $Mg^{2+}$ | $Ag^+$ | $Cd^{2+}$ | $Ga^{3+}$ |
| 0·18 | 0·094 | 1·72 | 1·09 | 0·20 |
| $K^+$ | $Ca^{2+}$ | $Au^+$ | $Hg^{2+}$ | $In^{3+}$ |
| 0·84 | 0·47 | 1·88 | 1·25 | 0·73 |
| $Rb^+$ | $Sr^{2+}$ | | | $Tl^{3+}$ |
| 1·42 | 0·86 | | | 0·87 |
| $Cs^+$ | $Ba^{2+}$ | | | |
| 2·44 | 1·56 | | | |
| $\alpha_-$ | | | | |
| $H^-$ | $F^-$ | $O^{2-}$ | | |
| 10·2 | 1·05 | 3·92 | | |
| | $Cl^-$ | $S^{2-}$ | | |
| | 3·69 | 10·3 | | |
| | $Br^-$ | $Se^{2-}$ | | |
| | 4·81 | 10·6 | | |
| | $I^-$ | $Te^{2-}$ | | |
| | 7·16 | 14·1 | | |

For the negative ion $Cl^-$, however, Mayer used a value

$$\alpha_{Cl} = 3 \cdot 45 \times 10^{-30} \, m^3,$$

calculated from the ultraviolet absorption spectrum of the crystal; this value differs somewhat from Pauling's.

Characteristic energies:

For the positive ion $Ag^+$, a value of $E_+$ equal to 90 per cent of the second ionization potential ($I_{II} = 21\cdot48$ eV) was used,

$$E_+ = 3\cdot10 \times 10^{-18} \text{ J molecule}^{-1}.$$

For the negative ion $Cl^-$, Mayer again used the experimental ultraviolet absorption to evaluate $E_-$, and obtained

$$E_- = 1\cdot56 \times 10^{-18} \text{ J molecule}^{-1}.$$

From these data,

$$C_{+-} = 9\cdot2 \times 10^{-78} \text{ J m}^6 \text{ molecule}^{-1}$$

$$C_{++} = 6\cdot9 \times 10^{-78} \text{ J m}^6 \text{ molecule}^{-1}$$

$$C_{--} = 13\cdot9 \times 10^{-78} \text{ J m}^6 \text{ molecule}^{-1}$$

and $\qquad C = 79\cdot5 \times 10^{-78} \text{ J m}^6 \text{ molecule}^{-1},$

so that $\qquad -\dfrac{C}{r_0^6} = -0\cdot175 \times 10^{-18} \text{ J molecule}^{-1}$

$$= -1\cdot09 \text{ eV}$$

$$= -106 \text{ kJ mol}^{-1} \text{ at } 0 \text{ K}.$$

Mayer added a further contribution, arising from dipole–quadrupole interaction in the crystal (these interactions are proportional to $1/r_0^8$ and are commonly between 10 and 20 per cent of the dipole–dipole term), amounting to $-19$ kJ mol$^{-1}$, so that the total dispersion or London energy

$$U_L = -125 \text{ kJ mol}^{-1}.$$

It is worthwhile to summarize the principal factors which tend to make the London energy high. They are:

(a) a high coordination number (cf. the summation constants in Table 17);

(b) a small internuclear distance;

(c) high values of the polarizabilities of the ions. The values in Table 18 are a general guide to this factor. Note that it is usually the *anion* whose polarizability has the dominating effect.

The polarizabilities of both cations and anions tend to increase down a periodic group, following the general increase in size and decrease in ionization potential (which reflect the increasing looseness with which the electrons are held) which occur as a group is descended. Thus caesium iodide contains the most polarizable of the alkali metal and halide ions, and furthermore crystallizes in $8:8$-coordination; these effects (which tend to increase the London energy) are partly offset by the relatively large internuclear distance.

*The zero-point energy*. A crystal at the absolute zero of temperature possesses a zero-point energy due to the persistence of the lattice vibrations at that temperature; according to the Debye theory of solids this energy, $U_Z$, is given by the relationship

$$U_Z = N_A \tfrac{9}{4} h \nu_{max},$$

where $N_A$ is the Avogadro number, $h$ is Planck's constant and $\nu_{max}$ is the Debye maximum frequency.

For most crystals composed of monatomic ions, $U_Z$ is of the order of $5\,kJ\,mol^{-1}$ and its inclusion is of doubtful significance in view of the errors inherent in the calculation of the other terms.

If the zero-point energy is included in the lattice energy, then $U$ is the sum of four terms,

$$U = U_C + U_B + U_L + U_Z,$$

where the sign of $U$, $U_C$ and $U_L$ is negative, and the sign of $U_B$ and $U_Z$ is positive.

**Table 19** Components of the Lattice Energy/(kJ mol$^{-1}$)

| Compound | $U_0$ (calc.) | $U_C$ | $U_B$ | $U_L$ | $U_Z$ | $\Delta H_{298}$ (calc.) | $\Delta H_{298}$ (from Born cycle) |
|---|---|---|---|---|---|---|---|
| NaCl | −766 | −863 | +114 | −25 | +8 | −776 | −787 |
| CsI | −580 | −619 | +90 | −54 | +3 | −592 | −602 |
| AgI | −795 | −808 | +138 | −128 | +3 | −807 | −891 |
| CuBr | −870 | −925 | +114 | −64 | +4 | −882 | −977 |

The contributions of $U_C$, $U_B$, $U_L$ and $U_Z$ to the lattice energies of a number of crystals are shown in Table 19. The agreement between the calculated lattice energy and that evaluated from the Born cycle is quite good for the alkali metal halides, sodium chloride and caesium iodide, for which the ionic model adopted is expected to be most satisfactory. For silver iodide and copper(I) bromide, however, the discrepancy is substantial, and it is generally agreed that in these crystals there will be a significant contribution from covalent binding forces. There is no straightforward means of allowing for such contributions in a term-by-term calculation.

## 3.4 Approximate expressions for the lattice energy

From the foregoing discussion it is clear that, before a start can be made on evaluating a lattice energy, it is necessary to know (or to be able to calculate) both the internuclear distance in the crystal and the appropriate Madelung constant. In cases where the experimental data are lacking, recourse must be had to tables of ionic radii in order to evaluate the likely internuclear distances, and crystal structures (and hence the Madelung constants) can often be guessed either from radius-ratio considerations, or from comparisons with chemically related compounds of known structure. Ionic radii are listed in Table 20; the value of both Pauling (P) and Goldschmidt (G) are given. In some cases the two sets of values differ and the choice between them is largely arbitrary.

Table 20   Ionic Radii, nm, for 6-fold Coordination

| | G | P | | G | P |
|---|---|---|---|---|---|
| $Ac^{3+}$ | | 0·118 | $Nd^{3+}$ | 0·115 | 0·108 |
| $Ag^{+}$ | 0·113 | 0·126 | $Ni^{2+}$ | 0·078 | 0·072 |
| $Ag^{2+}$ | | 0·089* | $Ni^{3+}$ | | 0·062 |
| $Al^{3+}$ | 0·057 | 0·050 | $Np^{3+}$ | | 0·109 |
| $Am^{3+}$ | | 0·106 | $Np^{4+}$ | | 0·095 |
| $Am^{4+}$ | | 0·092 | $O^{2-}$ | 0·132 | 0·140 |
| $As^{3+}$ | 0·069 | | $Os^{4+}$ | 0·067 | |
| $Au^{+}$ | | 0·137 | $Pa^{3+}$ | | 0·112 |
| $B^{3+}$ | | 0·020 | $Pa^{4+}$ | | 0·098 |
| $Ba^{2+}$ | 0·143 | 0·135 | $P^{3-}$ | | 0·212 |
| $Be^{2+}$ | 0·034 | 0·031 | $Pb^{2+}$ | 0·132 | 0·120 |
| $Bi^{3+}$ | | 0·096* | $Pd^{2+}$ | | 0·086 |
| $Br^{-}$ | 0·196 | 0·195 | $Pd^{4+}$ | | 0·065* |
| $Ca^{2+}$ | 0·106 | 0·099 | $Pr^{3+}$ | 0·116 | 0·109 |
| $Cd^{2+}$ | 0·103 | 0·097 | $Pr^{4+}$ | 0·100 | 0·092 |
| $Ce^{3+}$ | 0·118 | 0·111 | $Pu^{3+}$ | | 0·107 |
| $Ce^{4+}$ | 0·102 | 0·101 | $Pu^{4+}$ | | 0·093 |
| $Cl^{-}$ | 0·181 | 0·181 | $Pt^{2+}$ | | 0·080* |
| $Co^{2+}$ | 0·082 | 0·074 | $Pt^{4+}$ | | 0·065* |
| $Co^{3+}$ | 0·064 | 0·063 | $Ra^{2+}$ | 0·152 | 0·140 |
| $Cr^{2+}$ | 0·083 | 0·084 | $Rb^{+}$ | 0·149 | 0·148 |
| $Cr^{3+}$ | 0·064 | 0·069 | $Re^{4+}$ | | 0·072* |
| $Cs^{+}$ | 0·165 | 0·169 | $Rh^{3+}$ | 0·068 | |
| $Cu^{+}$ | | 0·096 | $Ru^{4+}$ | 0·065 | |
| $Cu^{2+}$ | | 0·072* | $S^{2-}$ | 0·174 | 0·184 |
| $Dy^{3+}$ | 0·107 | 0·099 | $Sb^{3+}$ | 0·090 | |
| $Er^{3+}$ | 0·104 | 0·096 | $Sc^{3+}$ | 0·083 | 0·081 |

| Ion | G | P | Ion | G | P |
|---|---|---|---|---|---|
| $Eu^{2+}$ | 0·124 | 0·112 | $Se^{2-}$ | 0·191 | 0·198 |
| $Eu^{3+}$ | 0·113 | 0·103 | $Sm^{3+}$ | 0·113 | 0·104 |
| $F^-$ | 0·133 | 0·136 | $Sn^{2+}$ | | 0·112 |
| $Fe^{2+}$ | 0·082 | 0·076 | $Sn^{4+}$ | 0·074 | 0·071 |
| $Fe^{3+}$ | 0·067 | 0·064 | $Sr^{2+}$ | 0·127 | 0·113 |
| $Ga^+$ | | 0·113 | $Tb^{3+}$ | 0·109 | 0·100 |
| $Ga^{3+}$ | 0·062 | 0·062 | $Tb^{4+}$ | 0·089 | |
| $Gd^{3+}$ | 0·111 | 0·102 | $Te^{2-}$ | 0·211 | 0·221 |
| $Ge^{2+}$ | 0·09 | 0·093 | $Th^{3+}$ | | 0·114 |
| $H^-$ | 0·154 | 0·208 | $Th^{4+}$ | 0·110 | |
| $Hf^{4+}$ | 0·084 | 0·081 | $Ti^{2+}$ | 0·080 | 0·090 |
| $Hg^{2+}$ | 0·112 | 0·110 | $Ti^{3+}$ | 0·069 | 0·076 |
| $Ho^{3+}$ | 0·105 | 0·097 | $Ti^{4+}$ | 0·064 | 0·068 |
| $In^+$ | | 0·132 | $Tl^+$ | 0·149 | 0·140 |
| $In^{3+}$ | 0·092 | 0·081 | $Tl^{3+}$ | 0·105 | 0·095 |
| $Ir^{4+}$ | 0·066 | | $Tm^{3+}$ | 0·104 | 0·095 |
| $I^-$ | 0·220 | 0·216 | $U^{3+}$ | | 0·111 |
| $K^+$ | 0·133 | 0·133 | $U^{4+}$ | 0·105 | 0·097 |
| $La^{3+}$ | 0·122 | 0·115 | $V^{2+}$ | 0·072 | 0·088 |
| $Li^+$ | 0·078 | 0·060 | $V^{3+}$ | 0·065 | 0·074 |
| $Lu^{3+}$ | 0·099 | 0·093 | $V^{4+}$ | 0·061 | 0·060 |
| $Mg^{2+}$ | 0·078 | 0·065 | $Y^{3+}$ | 0·106 | 0·093 |
| $Mn^{2+}$ | 0·091 | 0·080 | $Yb^{2+}$ | | 0·113 |
| $Mn^{3+}$ | 0·070 | 0·066 | $Yb^{3+}$ | 0·100 | 0·094 |
| $N^{3-}$ | | 0·171 | $Zn^{2+}$ | 0·083 | 0·074 |
| $NH^+$ | 0·143 | 0·148 | $Zr^{4+}$ | 0·087 | 0·080 |
| $Na^+$ | 0·098 | 0·095 | | | |

*Data*: Column G gives the original (1926) data of V. M. Goldschmidt.

Various revised tables of 'Goldschmidt radii' exist. The original figures were based on empirical internuclear distances in oxides and fluorides, with $O^{2-}$ and $F^-$ assigned the radii 0·132 and 0·133 nm respectively. Column P gives the radii assigned by L. Pauling (1960), with $O^{2-}$ = 0·140 nm and $F^-$ = 0·136 nm. Radii marked* are from L. H. Ahrens (1952).

### 3.4.1 *The Kapustinskii equations*

Kapustinskii (1956) has developed expressions for the lattice energy for use in cases where the experimental data are lacking. Kapustinskii's postulate is that there exists for any compound, whatever its crystal structure, an equivalent structure of the rock-salt type whose energy can be calculated by using the Madelung constant and ionic radii appropriate to the sixfold coordination of NaCl-type crystals.

The Kapustinskii expressions are derived either from the Born–Landé or the Born–Mayer equations and are respectively:

equation A $\quad U = \dfrac{N_A A e^2}{4\pi\varepsilon_0} \dfrac{v}{2} \dfrac{Z_c Z_a}{r_c + r_a} \left(1 - \dfrac{1}{n}\right),$

equation B $\quad U = \dfrac{N_A A e^2}{4\pi\varepsilon_0} \dfrac{v}{2} \dfrac{Z_c Z_a}{r_c + r_a} \left(1 - \dfrac{\rho}{r_c + r_a}\right),$

where $v$ is the number of ions in the simplest formula or stoichiometric 'molecule' – e.g. NaCl, $v = 2$; $CaF_2$, $v = 3$, etc.

$Z_c$, $Z_a$ are the numerical values of the charges on cation and anion – e.g. NaCl, $Z_c = +1$, $Z_a = -1$; $CaF_2$, $Z_c = +2$, $Z_a = -1$, etc.

$r_c$, $r_a$ are the ionic radii for octahedral coordination. In his own calculations, Kapustinskii used the original radii of Goldschmidt (see Table 20).

If a constant value of 9 is assumed for $n$ in equation A, and a constant value 0·0345 nm is likewise assumed for $\rho$ in equation B, and if the cation and anion radii $r_c$ and $r_a$ are expressed in nanometres, then the following equations are obtained in which the numerical constants have been collected and evaluated:

equation A $\quad U = 108\cdot0v \dfrac{Z_c Z_a}{r_c + r_a}$ kJ mol$^{-1}$,

equation B $\quad U = 121\cdot4v \dfrac{Z_c Z_a}{r_c + r_a} \left(1 - \dfrac{0\cdot0345}{r_c + r_a}\right)$ kJ mol$^{-1}$.

*Example.* Manganese(II) fluoride has the rutile structure, for which the Madelung constant $A$ is 4·816.

The experimental internuclear ($Mn^{2+}$–$F^-$) distance is 0·212 nm.

If the Born–Landé equation is used to evaluate the lattice energy,

$$U = \frac{N_A A z^2 e^2}{4\pi\varepsilon_0 r_0} \left(1 - \frac{1}{n}\right),$$

then with $z = 1$, $r_0 = 2\cdot12 \times 10^{-10}$ m, and $n = 8$,

$U = -2760$ kJ mol$^{-1}$.

If Kapustinskii's equation B is used,

$$U = 121\cdot4v \frac{Z_c Z_a}{r_c + r_a} \left(1 - \frac{\rho}{r_c + r_a}\right),$$

then with $Z_c = +2$, $Z_a = -1$, $v = 3$, $\rho = 0\cdot0345$ nm and the Goldschmidt radii (Table 20) $r_{Mn^{2+}} = 0\cdot091$ nm, and $r_{F^-} = 0\cdot133$ nm,

$U = -2750$ kJ mol$^{-1}$.

**83 Approximate Expressions for the Lattice Energy**

These results can be compared with the 'experimental' Born–Haber cycle value obtained as follows:

$$
\begin{array}{ll}
Mn(s) \rightarrow Mn(g) & \Delta h_1 \\
Mn(g) \rightarrow Mn^{2+}(g) + 2e & \Delta h_2 \\
F_2(g) \rightarrow 2F(g) & \Delta h_3 \\
2F(g) + 2e \rightarrow 2F^-(g) & \Delta h_4 \\
Mn^{2+}(g) + 2F^-(g) \rightarrow MnF_2(s) & \Delta h_5 \\
\hline
Mn(s) + F_2(g) \rightarrow MnF_2(s) & \Delta H_f^\circ \\
\hline
\end{array}
$$

$$\Delta h_5 = \Delta H_f^\circ - (\Delta h_1 + \Delta h_2 + \Delta h_3 + \Delta h_4).$$

Inserting experimental values:

$$\Delta h_5 = -791 - (281 + 2226 + 158 - 666)$$

$$= -2790 \text{ kJ mol}^{-1}.$$

In the above cycle, the figures used for $\Delta h_1$, $\Delta h_3$, and $\Delta H_f^\circ$ are values of $\Delta H_{298}^\circ$, while those for $\Delta h_2$ and $\Delta h_4$ are values of $\Delta U_0$. Where ionization energies and electron affinities are used in the same cycle involving the gain and loss of an equal number of electrons, the corrections necessary to adjust $\Delta U_0$ values to $\Delta H_{298}$ values cancel out and hence need not be made. The resulting $\Delta h_5$ is thus a lattice enthalpy at 298 K, while the values from the Born–Landé and Kapustinskii equations are strictly lattice energies at 0 K; in view of the approximations involved there is little point in making the small corrections to the latter values. It can be seen that in this case the calculated lattice energies are lower than the Born–Haber cycle result. This is usually found to be the case, since the calculated values do not explicitly take into account the attractive London forces.

The Kapustinskii equations are obviously very approximate; their value lies in providing a quick means of obtaining a guide to the likely magnitude of a lattice energy in cases where the experimental data necessary for more precise calculations are lacking.

3.4.2   *Thermochemical radii*

The Kapustinskii equations have been used in the following way to derive radii for ions – especially complex ions – for which no tabulated data exist.

Suppose it is desired to obtain for the sulphate ion $SO_4^{2-}$ a 'radius' which, when inserted in the Kapustinskii equation, will allow the evaluation of the lattice energy of a particular sulphate for which the cation radius is known. Then if two sulphates A and B are chosen – say A = $Na_2SO_4$ and B = $K_2SO_4$ – for which the heats of formation are known, it is easy to show that

$$U_A - U_B = [\Delta H_f^\circ(Na_2SO_4) - \Delta H_f^\circ(K_2SO_4)] - [2\Delta H_f^\circ, Na^+(g) - 2\Delta H_f^\circ, K^+(g)],$$

where $U$ is the lattice energy at 298 K and $\Delta H_f^\circ$ is the standard heat of formation of the species shown.

If the $\Delta H_f^\circ$ values are known, the lattice energy difference $U_A - U_B$ can be evaluated. $U_A - U_B$ can also be expressed as the difference between two Kapustinskii quantities, in which the only unknown is the anion radius $r_{SO_4^{2-}}$, which can thus be evaluated. The average results of this sort of manipulation have been called 'thermochemical radii' by Kapustinskii and Yatsimirskii, and some of them are listed in Table 21.

**Table 21** Thermochemical Radii (Nanometres)

| *anions* | | | | | |
|---|---|---|---|---|---|
| $NO_2^-$ | 0·155 | $HCOO^-$ | 0·158 | $BeF_4^{2-}$ | 0·245 |
| $NO_3^-$ | 0·189 | $CH_3COO^-$ | 0·159 | $BO_3^{3-}$ | 0·191 |
| $NH_2^-$ | 0·130 | $HCO_3^-$ | 0·163 | $MnO_4^-$ | 0·240 |
| picrate | 0·223 | $CO_3^{2-}$ | 0·185 | $MoO_4^{2-}$ | 0·254 |
| $ClO_3^-$ | 0·200 | $OCN^-$ | 0·159 | $CrO_4^{2-}$ | 0·240 |
| $ClO_4^-$ | 0·236 | $SCN^-$ | 0·195 | $O_2^{2-}$ | 0·180 |
| $BrO_3^-$ | 0·191 | $CN^-$ | 0·182 | $PO_4^{3-}$ | 0·238 |
| $IO_3^-$ | 0·182 | $SO_4^{2-}$ | 0·230 | $AsO_4^{3-}$ | 0·248 |
| $IO_4^-$ | 0·249 | $SeO_4^{2-}$ | 0·243 | $SbO_4^{3-}$ | 0·260 |
| $OH^-$ | 0·140 | $TeO_4^{2-}$ | 0·254 | $BiO_4^{3-}$ | 0·268 |
| $SH^-$ | 0·195 | $BF_4^-$ | 0·228 | $SiO_4^{4-}$ | 0·24 |

| *cations* | | | | | |
|---|---|---|---|---|---|
| $Mn(H_2O)_6^{2+}$ | 0·234 | $Mn(NH_3)_6^{2+}$ | 0·265 | $Co(NH_3)_5Cl^{2+}$ | 0·236 |
| $Co(H_2O)_6^{2+}$ | 0·234 | $Fe(NH_3)_6^{2+}$ | 0·263 | $N(CH_3)_4^+$ | 0·300 |
| $Ni(H_2O)_6^{2+}$ | 0·229 | $Co(NH_3)_6^{2+}$ | 0·260 | | |
| $Zn(H_2O)_6^{2+}$ | 0·235 | $Ni(NH_3)_6^{2+}$ | 0·258 | | |
| $Mg(H_2O)_6^{2+}$ | 0·235 | $Zn(NH_3)_6^{2+}$ | 0·264 | | |
| | | $Cd(NH_3)_6^{2+}$ | 0·266 | | |

Data from A. F. Kapustinskii (1956) and references therein.

3.5 **Periodic trends in $\Delta G_f^\circ$ and $\Delta H_f^\circ$ for ionic crystals**

It is often of interest to make an analysis of the factors responsible for the *trends* in the free energies and enthalpies of formation observable in passing down the vertical groups, or across the horizontal periods of the periodic table. For example, values of $\Delta G_f^\bullet$ and $\Delta H_f^\circ$ for the alkali metal halides are given in Table 22. The entropy contributions to the free energy of formation, $T\Delta S_f^\circ$, are also shown.

**Table 22**  Thermodynamic Data for Alkali Metal Halides at 298 K

| | $\Delta G_f^{\circ}/(\text{kJ mol}^{-1})$ | $\Delta H_f^{\circ}/(\text{kJ mol}^{-1})$ | $T\,\Delta S_f^{\circ}/(\text{kJ mol}^{-1})$ |
|---|---|---|---|
| LiF | −584 | −612 | −28 |
| LiCl | −384 | −409 | −25 |
| LiBr | −340 | −350 | −10·5 |
| LiI | −268 | −271 | −3·3 |
| NaF | −541 | −569 | −28 |
| NaCl | −384 | −411 | −27 |
| NaBr | −348 | −360 | −12·1 |
| NaI | −282 | −288 | −5·4 |
| KF | −533 | −563 | −30 |
| KCl | −408 | −436 | −28 |
| KBr | −379 | −392 | −13·0 |
| KI | −322 | −328 | −5·4 |
| RbF | −520 | −549 | −30 |
| RbCl | −405 | −430 | −26 |
| RbBr | −378 | −389 | −10·9 |
| RbI | −326 | −328 | −5·4 |
| CsF | −500 | −531 | −31 |
| CsCl | −404 | −433 | −29 |
| CsBr | −383 | −395 | −11·3 |
| CsI | −333 | −337 | −3·3 |

The following points are noteworthy:

(a) The value of $T\,\Delta S_f^{\circ}$ is negative in all cases, so that each of the formation reactions

$$M(s) + \tfrac{1}{2}X_2 \text{ (standard state)} \rightarrow MX(s),$$

where X = F, Cl, Br, I, and M = Li, Na, K, Rb, Cs, is accompanied by a decrease in entropy. This entropy loss is greatest ($T\,\Delta S_f^{\circ} = 25 - 30\,\text{kJ}$ $\text{mol}^{-1}$) when $X_2 = F_2(g)$ and $Cl_2(g)$, that is when the reaction involves the conversion of randomly distributed gas molecules into components of highly ordered crystalline solids. The decrease in entropy is less marked where the reacting halogen is a liquid in its standard state ($Br_2$), and quite small ($T\,\Delta S_f^{\circ} = 2·9 - 5·4\,\text{kJ mol}^{-1}$) when the reactant is solid iodine.

(b) The enthalpy change $\Delta H_f^{\circ}$ is in all cases numerically much larger than the $T\,\Delta S_f^{\circ}$ term, and its contribution dominates $\Delta G_f^{\circ}$. Hence the trend in $\Delta G_f^{\circ}$, either for the halides of a given alkali metal, or for the alkali metals with a given halide partner, is closely related to (and in effect determined by) the trend in $\Delta H_f^{\circ}$.

(c) For a given alkali metal, the order of exothermicity of formation is in all cases $F^- > Cl^- > Br^- > I^-$. The reasons for this order can be discerned from an analysis of the terms contributing to $\Delta H_f^\circ$, as can be seen from the following data for the sodium halides:

*Terms, $\Delta H_{298}^\circ/(kJ\ mol^{-1})$, contributing to the enthalpies of formation of the sodium halides NaX.*

|  | F | Cl | Br | I |
|---|---|---|---|---|
| $Na(s) \rightarrow Na(g)$ | 108 | 108 | 108 | 108 |
| $Na(g) \rightarrow Na^+(g)+e$ | 502 | 502 | 502 | 502 |
| $Na(s) \rightarrow Na^+(g)+e$ $\quad = \Delta H_f^\circ,\ Na^+(g)$ | 610 | 610 | 610 | 610 |
| $\frac{1}{2}X_2$ (standard state) $\rightarrow \frac{1}{2}X_2(g)$ | 0 | 0 | 15 | 31 |
| $\frac{1}{2}X_2(g) \rightarrow X(g)$ | 79 | 121 | 97 | 75 |
| $X(g)+e \rightarrow X^-(g)$ | −339 | −354 | −330 | −301 |
| $\frac{1}{2}X_2$ (standard state)$+e \rightarrow X^-(g)$ $\quad = \Delta H_f^\circ,\ X^-(g)$ | −260 | −233 | −218 | −195 |
| $Na^+(g)+X^-(g) \rightarrow NaX(s)$ $\quad = \Delta H_{lattice}^\circ$ | −919 | −787 | −752 | −703 |
| $Na(s)+\frac{1}{2}X_2$ (standard state) $\rightarrow$ $\quad NaX(s) = \Delta H_f^\circ,\ Na^+(g)$ $\quad +\Delta H_f^\circ,\ X^-(g)+\Delta H_{lattice}^\circ$ | −569 | −410 | −360 | −288 |

These data indicate that $\Delta H_f^\circ$ for a sodium halide is the sum of enthalpies of formation of the gaseous ions $Na^+$ and $X^-$ from the elements in their standard states, and the lattice enthalpy $\Delta H_{lattice}^\circ$. Of course $\Delta H_f^\circ$, $Na^+(g)$ is constant, but $\Delta H_f^\circ$, $X^-(g)$ becomes decreasingly negative from $X^- = F^-$ to $X^- = I^-$, for reasons apparent from the data. The high negative value for $F^-$ is largely a consequence of the ease of fission of the covalent bond in $F_2(g)$, that is of the low heat of atomization of the fluorine molecule.

The trend in lattice enthalpies, which also become decreasingly negative from $X^- = F^-$ to $X^- = I^-$, is in the same direction. This trend is obviously due to the increase in internuclear distance in the crystal accompanying the increase in anion radius from $F^-$ ($r = 0.136$ nm) to $I^-$ ($r = 0.216$ nm); the electrostatic attraction between the oppositely charged ions in the crystal will obviously diminish as the interionic distance becomes larger.

(d) The trend in $\Delta H_f^\circ$ down the alkali metal group for a given halide partner is not consistently in the same direction – for example $\Delta H_f^\circ$ for the alkali metal iodides MI *increases* from M = Li to M = Cs, while for the fluorides the trend is in the reverse direction; the trend is irregular for the chlorides and bromides.

The terms, $\Delta H_{298}^{\circ}/(\text{kJ mol}^{-1})$, contributing to $\Delta H_f^{\circ}$ for the iodides and fluorides are as follows:

|  | Li | Na | K | Rb | Cs |
|---|---|---|---|---|---|
| *iodides* | | | | | |
| M(s) → M(g) | 161 | 108 | 90 | 82 | 78 |
| M(g) → M$^+$(g) + e | 526 | 502 | 424 | 408 | 381 |
| $\Delta H_f^{\circ}$, M$^+$(g) | 687 | 610 | 514 | 490 | 459 |
| $\frac{1}{2}$I$_2$(s)　　　　→ I$^-$(g) | −195 | −195 | −195 | −195 | −195 |
| M$^+$(g) + I$^-$(g) → MI(s) | −763 | −703 | −647 | −624 | −601 |
| $\Delta H_f^{\circ}$, MI(s) | −271 | −288 | −328 | −329 | −337 |
| | | | | | |
| *fluorides* | | | | | |
| M(s)　　　　→ M$^+$(g) | 687 | 610 | 514 | 490 | 459 |
| $\frac{1}{2}$F$_2$(g)　　→ F$^-$(g) | −260 | −260 | −260 | −260 | −260 |
| M$^+$(g) + F$^-$(g) → MF(s) | −1039 | −919 | −817 | −779 | −730 |
| $\Delta H_f^{\circ}$, MF(s) | −612 | −569 | −563 | −549 | −531 |

For a given halide (i.e. for constant $\Delta H_f^{\circ}$, X$^-$(g)) $\Delta H_f^{\circ}$, MX(s) is determined by the balance between $\Delta H_f^{\circ}$, M$^+$(g) and the lattice enthalpy. From the data quoted it can be seen that for the alkali metals, $\Delta H_f^{\circ}$, M$^+$(g) becomes decreasingly positive from M = Li to M = Cs, a trend which follows the increasing ease of sublimation of the metal and ionization of the gaseous atom. The lattice enthalpies also follow a regular trend and become decreasingly negative as the group is descended and the radius of the metal cation increases. In the case of the fluorides the balance of these two trends is such as to produce a decreasingly negative heat of formation of the solid halide, while in the case of the iodides the balance is in the reverse direction.

It is only by considering the factors contributing to $\Delta H_f^{\circ}$ in this way that the causes of variations in heats of formation down the periodic groups can be traced.

### 3.5.1 *Trends in $\Delta H_f^{\circ}$ across the first transition series*

The enthalpies of formation of the dichlorides of the metals of the first transition series are as follows:

$\Delta H_f^\circ$, $MCl_2(s)/(kJ\ mol^{-1})$

| Ca | Ti | V | Cr | Mn | Fe | Co | Ni | Cu | Zn |
|---|---|---|---|---|---|---|---|---|---|
| $-798$ | $-504$ | $-489$ | $-397$ | $-473$ | $-341$ | $-326$ | $-305$ | $-209$ | $-416$ |

The terms which contribute to $\Delta H_f^\circ$ are:

| A. Endothermic terms: | Ca | Ti | V | Cr | Mn |
|---|---|---|---|---|---|
| $M(s) \rightarrow M(g)$ | 177 | 473 | 515 | 397 | 281 |
| $M(g) \rightarrow M^{2+}(g)+2e$ | 1746 | 1979 | 2075 | 2256 | 2238 |
| $\Delta H_f^\circ$, $M^{2+}(g)$ | 1923 | 2452 | 2590 | 2653 | 2519 |

| B. Exothermic terms: | | | | | |
|---|---|---|---|---|---|
| $Cl_2(g)+2e \rightarrow 2Cl^-(g)$ | $-467$ | $-467$ | $-467$ | $-467$ | $-467$ |
| $M^{2+}(g)+2Cl^-(g) \rightarrow MCl_2(s)$ | $-2254$ | $-2489$ | $-2612$ | $-2583$ | $-2525$ |
| | $-2721$ | $-2956$ | $-3079$ | $-3050$ | $-2992$ |
| $A+B = \Delta H^\circ$, $MCl_2(s)$ | $-798$ | $-504$ | $-489$ | $-397$ | $-473$ |

| A. Endothermic terms: | Fe | Co | Ni | Cu | Zn |
|---|---|---|---|---|---|
| $M(s) \rightarrow M(g)$ | 416 | 425 | 430 | 340 | 126 |
| $M(g) \rightarrow M^{2+}(g)+2e$ | 2331 | 2414 | 2500 | 2714 | 2650 |
| $\Delta H_f^\circ$, $M^{2+}(g)$ | 2747 | 2839 | 2930 | 3054 | 2776 |

| B. Exothermic terms | | | | | |
|---|---|---|---|---|---|
| $Cl_2(g)+2e \rightarrow 2Cl^-(g)$ | $-467$ | $-467$ | $-467$ | $-467$ | $-467$ |
| $M^{2+}(g)+2Cl^-(g) \rightarrow MCl_2(s)$ | $-2621$ | $-2698$ | $-2768$ | $-2796$ | $-2725$ |
| | $-3088$ | $-3165$ | $-3235$ | $-3263$ | $-3192$ |
| $A+B = \Delta H_f^\circ$, $MCl_2(s)$ | $-341$ | $-326$ | $-305$ | $-209$ | $-416$ |

The heat of formation of each solid dichloride, $\Delta H_f^\circ$, $MCl_2(s)$, is in effect the resultant of:
A. two endothermic contributions—the heat of sublimation of the metal, and the much greater heat of ionization of the gaseous metal atom; together these two heat terms are equivalent to the heat of formation of the gaseous metal cation, $\Delta H_f^\circ$, $M^{2+}(g)$; and
B. two exothermic contributions – the constant heat of formation of the gaseous anions, $\Delta H_f^\circ$, $2Cl^-(g)$, and the lattice enthalpy.

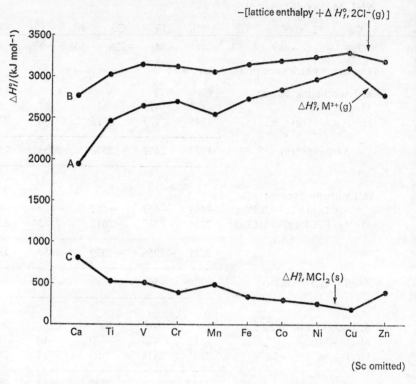

−[lattice enthalpy −+Δ $H_f^o$, 2Cl$^-$(g)]

$\Delta H_f^o$, M$^{2+}$(g)

$\Delta H_f^o$, MCl$_2$(s)

Ca  Ti  V  Cr  Mn  Fe  Co  Ni  Cu  Zn

(Sc omitted)

Figure 12

The contributions $A$ and $B$ are plotted in Figure 12. The plot of the data for $A(\Delta H_f^o$, M$^{2+}$(g)) is characterized by three noticeably low values – at calcium, manganese and zinc. The heats of sublimation and ionization are both rather small for these metals: in the case of the heat of ionization, the low values are presumably related to the relative ease of formation of Ca$^{2+}$(g), which has a noble gas configuration; Mn$^{2+}$(g), which has a $3d^5$ configuration, and Zn$^{2+}$(g), which has a $3d^{10}$ configuration. The data for $B$ – which combine the lattice enthalpy with the constant heat of formation of the gaseous anion – also show the same characteristically low values for calcium, manganese and zinc, for reasons to be discussed shortly. The resultant of $A$ and $B$, that is the heat of formation of the solid dichloride, $\Delta H_f^o$, MCl$_2$(s), is shown for each metal in plot $C$.

The trend in lattice enthalpies from calcium to zinc is of considerable theoretical interest. The dipositive metal ions from Ca$^{2+}$ to Zn$^{2+}$ possess a set of $3d$ orbitals whose electron population increases from zero (Ca$^{2+}$) to ten ($Zn^{2+}$). The five $3d$ orbitals are degenerate in the isolated gas-phase ions, or where the ions are subject to a superimposed electrostatic field of spherical symmetry. In the crystalline dichlorides, however, the cations $M^{2+}$ are affected by the octahedral electrostatic field of the surrounding chloride ions, and their $3d$ orbitals are no longer degenerate. In the presence of the octahedral crystal field, the five $3d$ orbitals (see Figure 13) divide into two groups separated by an energy difference $\Delta$; the group of higher energy comprises the two $3d$ orbitals whose lobes are directed *along* the $x$-, $y$- and $z$-axes, viz the $3d_{x^2-y^2}$ and $3d_{z^2}$ orbitals (designated $e_g$ orbitals), while the group of lower energy comprises the three $3d$ orbitals whose lobes are directed *between* the octahedral axes, viz the $3d_{xy}$, $3d_{yz}$ and $3d_{xz}$ orbitals (designated $t_{2g}$ orbitals).

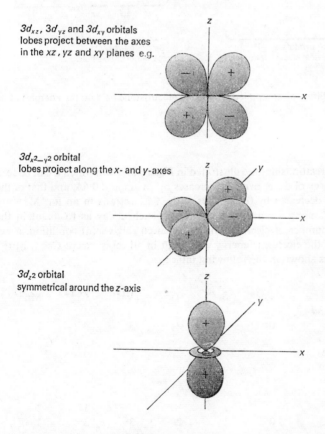

$3d_{xz}$, $3d_{yz}$ and $3d_{xy}$ orbitals
lobes project between the axes
in the $xz$, $yz$ and $xy$ planes e.g.

$3d_{x^2-y^2}$ orbital
lobes project along the $x$- and $y$-axes

$3d_{z^2}$ orbital
symmetrical around the $z$-axis

Figure 13  Spatial distribution of $3d$ orbitals. The surfaces represented include most of the electron density. The sign of the wave function in each region is shown

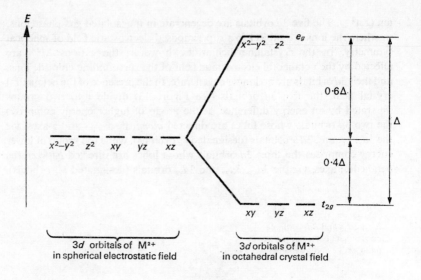

Figure 14 Effect of an applied octahedral electrostatic field on the energies of 3*d* orbitals

The energy relationships are illustrated in Figure 14, from which it can be seen that the energy of the $e_g$ orbitals increases by an amount $0.6\Delta$, and that of the $t_{2g}$ orbitals decreases by $0.4\Delta$. Thus if the 3*d* electrons in an ion $M^{2+}$ are distributed among the available orbitals in such a way as to maintain the maximum number of electrons in the unpaired (high-spin) condition, a net lowering of the electronic energy will result in all cases except $Ca^{2+}$, $Mn^{2+}$ and $Zn^{2+}$ as shown in the following table:

|  | $Ca^{2+}$ | $Sc^{2+}$ | $Ti^{2+}$ | $V^{2+}$ | $Cr^{2+}$ | $Mn^{2+}$ |
|---|---|---|---|---|---|---|
| Number of 3*d* electrons | 0 | 1 | 2 | 3 | 4 | 5 |
| Distribution for high-spin configuration: |  |  |  |  |  |  |
| $e_g$ |  |  |  |  | 1 | 2 |
| $t_{2g}$ | 0 | 1 | 2 | 3 | 3 | 3 |
| Lowering of energy | 0 | $0.4\Delta$ | $0.8\Delta$ | $1.2\Delta$ | $0.6\Delta$ | 0 |

| | $Fe^{2+}$ | $Co^{2+}$ | $Ni^{2+}$ | $Cu^{2+}$ | $Zn^{2+}$ |
|---|---|---|---|---|---|
| Number of $3d$ electrons | 6 | 7 | 8 | 9 | 10 |
| Distribution for high-spin configuration: | | | | | |
| $e_g$ | 2 | 2 | 2 | 3 | 4 |
| $t_{2g}$ | 4 | 5 | 6 | 6 | 6 |
| Lowering of energy | $0.4\Delta$ | $0.8\Delta$ | $1.2\Delta$ | $0.6\Delta$ | 0 |

According to this simple electrostatic interpretation, all the $M^{2+}$ ions (with the exception of $Ca^{2+}$, $Mn^{2+}$ and $Zn^{2+}$) will, when subjected to an octahedral crystal field, be stabilized to an extent which must be reflected in the lattice energy of the crystal. The resulting 'crystal field stabilization energy' is thus superimposed on the various factors described earlier in this chapter as contributing to the lattice energy.

The lattice enthalpies for the transition metal dichlorides are plotted in Figure 15. It is reasonable to suppose that the smooth curve (it is almost a straight line) drawn through $CaCl_2$, $MnCl_2$ and $ZnCl_2$ will represent the lattice enthalpies of all the dichlorides *in the absence of any crystal field stabilization*, since the ions $Ca^{2+}$, $Mn^{2+}$ and $Zn^{2+}$, as shown above, are not stabilized by a superimposed octahedral field. The differences $x$ between this curve and the experimental curve lying above it will thus reflect the extent of the crystal field stabilization. These differences are as follows:

| $MCl_2$ M = | Ca | Sc | Ti | V | Cr | Mn | Fe | Co | Ni | Cu | Zn |
|---|---|---|---|---|---|---|---|---|---|---|---|
| $x$/(kJ mol$^{-1}$) | 0 | ? | 120 | 190 | 100 | 0 | 50 | 90 | 115 | 105 | 0 |

It is interesting to compare these figures with the results obtained from experimental absorption spectra; the absorption of light accompanying transitions between the $t_{2g}$ and $e_g$ orbitals provides a measure of the energy difference $\Delta$ between them. For example, $NiCl_2(s)$ has an experimental absorption maximum at 927 mm$^{-1}$. Since the wave number corresponding to an energy of one electron volt is 806·6 mm$^{-1}$, and 1 eV = 96·5 kJ mol$^{-1}$ the absorption maximum of 927 mm$^{-1}$ indicates a crystal field splitting ($\Delta$) of (927/806·6) 96·5 kJ mol$^{-1}$. The crystal field stabilization energy for the $d^8$ $Ni^{2+}$ ion in an octahedral field is thus

$$1.2\Delta = \frac{927\,000}{806\,600} \times 96.5 \times 1.2 = 133 \text{ kJ mol}^{-1},$$

in reasonable agreement with the stabilization deduced from Figure 15, viz 115 kJ mol$^{-1}$.

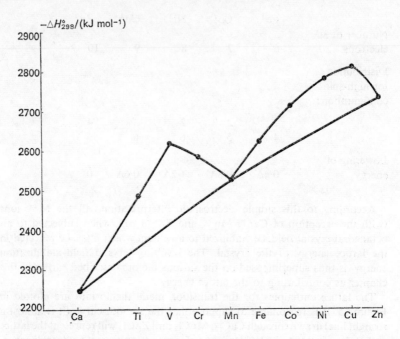

Figure 15 Lattice enthalpies for transition metal dichlorides $-\Delta H^{\circ}_{298}$ for $M^{2+}(g) + 2Cl^-(g) \rightarrow MCl_2(s)$

It should be noted that the foregoing interpretation is wholly electrostatic, and neglects the other contributions (for example, both $\sigma$ and $\pi$ covalent bonding) which are taken into account in the more elaborate 'ligand field' theory of coordination compounds.

### 3.6    Melting points and boiling points of ionic crystals

It is well known that in general the melting points and boiling points of ionic substances tend to be very much higher than those of substances composed of covalent molecules; substances in the former class are generally solids at room temperature, while those in the latter class are commonly gases or liquids. Thus the ionic, non-molecular sodium chloride melts at 1074 K and boils at 1738 K, while the molecular, covalent $TiCl_4$ melts at 250 K and boils at 410 K. Ionic substances, in the solid and liquid phases, are composed of ions between which strong electrostatic forces of attraction exist. These forces present a relatively formidable energetic obstacle to the processes of melting and vaporization. In the case of molecular compounds, however, the structural units are covalent molecules: the intramolecular binding forces – strong covalent bonds – are little affected by the processes of fusion and vaporization, which are accompanied by a loosening of the relatively weak intermolecular (van der Waals) forces of attraction. For both classes of compound, fusion and particularly vaporization are changes which, when conducted under standard conditions, are accompanied by increases in entropy, as discussed in section 1.4.3; it is therefore necessary to examine both the enthalpy and entropy changes when discussing melting and boiling points.

**Table 23**  Enthalpies and Entropies of Fusion and Vaporization of Inorganic Substances

| Substance | m.p./K | $\Delta H_{fusion}$ /(kJ mol$^{-1}$) at m.p. | $\Delta S_{fusion}$ /(J K$^{-1}$ mol$^{-1}$) at m.p. | b.p./K | $\Delta H_{vap}$ /(kJ mol$^{-1}$) at b.p. | $\Delta S_{vap}$ /(J K$^{-1}$ mol$^{-1}$) at b.p. |
|---|---|---|---|---|---|---|
| *Class* 1: *ionic compounds* | | | | | | |
| NaCl | 1074 | 29 | 27 | 1738 | 170 | 98 |
| CaF$_2$ | 1691 | 30 | 18 | 2773 | 310 | 112 |
| MgCl$_2$ | 988 | 43 | 44 | 1691 | 137 | 81 |
| PbI$_2$ | 685 | 25 | 37 | 1145 | 103 | 90 |
| LiBr | 823 | 12 | 15 | 1583 | 148 | 94 |
| ZnCl$_2$ | 556 | 23 | 41 | 1005 | 119 | 119 |
| FeCl$_2$ | 950 | 43 | 45 | 1285 | 126 | 98 |
| BaF$_2$ | 1593 | 13 | 8 | 2488 | 280 | 113 |
| AgCl | 728 | 13 | 18 | 1837 | 178 | 97 |
| *Class* 2: *molecular (covalent) substances* | | | | | | |
| H$_2$S | 187·5 | 2·5 | 13 | 212·6 | 19 | 88 |
| H$_2$O | 273 | 6·0 | 22 | 373 | 41 | 110 |
| NH$_3$ | 195 | 5·6 | 29 | 239·5 | 23 | 97 |
| TiCl$_4$ | 250 | 9·4 | 38 | 410 | 36 | 88 |
| PCl$_3$ | 182 | 4·5 | 25 | 348 | 31 | 88 |
| Br$_2$ | 265·7 | 10·5 | 40 | 331 | 31 | 94 |
| SnBr$_4$ | 303 | 11·9 | 39 | 480 | 41 | 85 |
| SO$_2$ | 197·5 | 7·4 | 38 | 263 | 25 | 95 |
| SiH$_4$ | 88 | 0·7 | 8 | 161 | 13 | 77 |

Some typical thermodynamic data for ionic and molecular substances are given in Table 23. The following general points emerge from a consideration of these data:

(a) For a given compound of either class, the heat absorbed on vaporization is considerably greater than that absorbed on fusion, indicating that when the liquid boils the decrease in bond strength is greater than when the corresponding solid melts.

(b) Heats of fusion and vaporization are distinctly greater for compounds of class 1 than for those of class 2, indicating that the processes of melting and boiling involve a bigger disruption of bonding for ionic compounds than for covalent molecular compounds. This circumstance is related to the fact that in the latter (class 2) compounds only intermolecular van der Waals forces are broken down, while in the former (class 1) compounds, much stronger electrostatic forces must be overcome.

(c) For a given compound of either class, the entropy increase on vaporization is much greater than that on fusion. However, for the examples quoted there are no easily discernible differences between classes 1 and 2 in respect of the magnitude of the entropy changes.

Therefore since

$$T/K \text{ (m.p.)} = \frac{\Delta H_{\text{fusion}}}{\Delta S_{\text{fusion}}} \quad \text{and} \quad T/K \text{ (b.p.)} = \frac{\Delta H_{\text{vap}}}{\Delta S_{\text{vap}}},$$

the generally higher values of $T$ for the ionic compounds of class 1 are determined essentially by the fact that the enthalpy changes $\Delta H_{\text{fusion}}$ and $\Delta H_{\text{vap}}$ are greater, that is by the fact that stronger binding forces must be overcome in the processes of melting and boiling. Nevertheless the data for individual compounds repay examination; for example, it is interesting that LiBr and $SnBr_4$ have very similar values of $\Delta H_{\text{fusion}}$, and that the higher melting point of LiBr (823 K; cf. $SnBr_4$, 303 K) is related to the much smaller molar entropy of fusion of that compound.

3.7    **Estimation of $\Delta G_f^\circ$ for ionic compounds**

The estimation of $\Delta G_f^\circ$ for ionic compounds usually involves the separate estimation of the contributing enthalpy ($\Delta H_{298}^\circ$) and entropy ($T \Delta S_{298}^\circ$) terms. The need for estimates of this sort arises in a number of situations – sometimes simply because the necessary measurements have not been made, more frequently because the compound in question has not, for one reason or another, ever been prepared. It may be that the synthesis of a new compound is contemplated and the thermodynamic feasibility of a preparative method requires testing; or it may be that the compound is one which has defied preparation for no immediately obvious reason (e.g. AuF, $AsCl_5$) or is one of some theoretical interest (e.g. HeF, CaCl). The separate estimation of $\Delta H_f^\circ$ and $\Delta S_f^\circ$ will now be discussed.

## 3.7.1 Estimation of $\Delta H_f^\circ$

For ionic compounds, the basic thermodynamic data required are the heats of formation (from elements in their standard states) of the gaseous cation and anion, and the lattice enthalpy. Thus for a salt $M^+X^-$,

$$\Delta H_f^\circ, MX(s) = \Delta H_f^\circ, M^+(g) + \Delta H_f^\circ, X^-(g) + \Delta H_{lattice}^\circ.$$

Of these contributing terms, the lattice enthalpy has already been discussed in some detail. The heat of formation of the gaseous cation is, in the case of a monatomic species, the sum of a heat of atomization and a heat of ionization, and the appropriate experimental data (heats of sublimation of metals, and ionization potentials) are available in most cases. In the case of monatomic anions, the heat of formation is similarly the sum of a heat of atomization and an electron affinity, and again the experimental data are available for common species such as the halide anions. However, where the cation or anion is complex, the two component heat quantities are rarely available; for example, $\Delta H_f^\circ, ClO_4^-(g)$ is the sum of the enthalpies of the reactions

$$\tfrac{1}{2}Cl_2(g) + 2O_2(g) \rightarrow ClO_4(g)$$

$$ClO_4(g) + e \rightarrow ClO_4^-(g),$$

neither of which is experimentally accessible because of the non-existence of the radical $ClO_4(g)$. In such cases $\Delta H_f^\circ$ for a complex cation or anion can be obtained provided the lattice enthalpy of a salt of known $\Delta H_f^\circ$ can be calculated, and the heat of formation of the other gaseous ion is known.

For example, an average value for the enthalpy of formation of the cobalt(II) hexammine cation $Co(NH_3)_6^{2+}$ can be assessed from data on the dihalides as follows:

$$\Delta H_f^\circ, Co(NH_3)_6^{2+}(g) = \Delta H_f^\circ, Co(NH_3)_6X_2(s) - \Delta H_f^\circ, 2X^-(g) - \Delta H_{lattice}^\circ.$$

The lattice enthalpies are computed using Kapustinskii's equation B (section 3.4.1), with the radii $Co(NH_3)_6^{2+} = 0.260$ nm, $Cl^- = 0.181$ nm, $Br^- = 0.196$ nm, and $I^- = 0.220$ nm, and the approximate relationship $\Delta H_{lattice}^\circ \approx \Delta U_0 - 2RT$. The enthalpies of formation of $X^-(g)$ and $Co(NH_3)_6X_2(s)$ are literature values:

| X | $\Delta H_f^\circ$/(kJ mol$^{-1}$)<br>$Co(NH_3)_6X_2(s)$ | $\Delta H_f^\circ$/(kJ mol$^{-1}$)<br>$2X^-(g)$ | lattice<br>enthalpy,<br>/(kJ mol$^{-1}$) | $\Delta H_f^\circ$/(kJ mol$^{-1}$)<br>$Co(NH_3)_6^{2+}(g)$ |
|---|---|---|---|---|
| Cl | $-1005$ | $-467$ | $-1528$ | $+990$ |
| Br | $-932$ | $-436$ | $-1482$ | $+985$ |
| I | $-808$ | $-389$ | $-1414$ | $+995$ |

whence $\Delta H_f^\circ, Co(NH_3)_6^{2+}(g) = 990 \pm 10$ kJ mol$^{-1}$.

## 97 Estimation of $\Delta G_f^\circ$ for Ionic Compounds

o

A number of values of $\Delta H_f^\circ$ for gaseous complex anions are collected in Table 24.

**Table 24**  $\Delta H_f^\circ/(\text{kJ mol}^{-1})$ for Complex Anions

| $OH^-$ | $NH^{2-}$ | $C_2^{2-}$ | $NH_2^-$ | $BH_4^-$ | $HF_2^-$ | $SO_4^{2-}$ |
|--------|-----------|------------|----------|----------|----------|-------------|
| 209 | 1092 | $-1025$ | 63 | $-96$ | 628 | $-741$ |
| $SH^-$ | $CN^-$ | $N_3^-$ | $NO_3^-$ | $BF_4^-$ | $NCO^-$ | $SeO_4^{2-}$ |
| $-130$ | 29 | 146 | $-339$ | $-1699$ | $-264$ | $-502$ |

Data from T. C. Waddington (1959), and, for $SO_4^{2-}$ and $SeO_4^{2-}$ from M. F. C. Ladd and W. H. Lee (1961).

### 3.7.2  *Estimation of $\Delta S_f^\circ$*

The estimation of $\Delta S_f^\circ$ for an ionic compound requires a knowledge of the entropy $S_{298}^\circ$ of the compound and of the constituent elements in their standard states. Experimental values of the latter are listed in Table 25.

Latimer has provided a rough means of assessing the value of $S_{298}^\circ$ for ionic compounds by tabulating the average contributions made by various ions to the total entropy of the solid. These contributions are listed in Table 26. In the case of anions the contribution depends on the ionic charge. In the case of complex salts, for example, $K_2IrCl_6$, the contribution chosen for Cl is that corresponding to the average charge on the metals considered as monatomic cations ($2K^+$, $Ir^{4+}$, average charge $= 2+$).

*Example.* Estimate the free energy of formation $\Delta G_f^\circ$ of the hypothetical caesium(II) fluoride, $CsF_2(s)$.

The required reaction sequence is

| | | |
|---|---|---|
| (i) | | $Cs(s) \rightarrow Cs(g)$ |
| (ii) | | $Cs(g) \rightarrow Cs^{2+}(g) + 2e$ |
| (iii) | | $F_2(g) \rightarrow 2F(g)$ |
| (iv) | | $2F(g) + 2e \rightarrow 2F^-(g)$ |
| (v) | $Cs^{2+}(g) + 2F^-(g) \rightarrow CsF_2(s)$ | |

| | |
|---|---|
| (vi) | $Cs(s) + F_2(g) \rightarrow CsF_2(s)$ |

$\Delta H_f^\circ$, $CsF_2(s)$:

Experimental data are available for the enthalpies of steps (i, ii, iii and iv). It remains, therefore, to estimate $\Delta H_{298}^\circ$ for reaction (v) (the lattice enthalpy), and this can be done with sufficient accuracy using Kapustinskii's method.

**Table 25** Entropies of Elements in Their Standard States at 298 K, $S^\circ_{298}$/(J K$^{-1}$ mol$^{-1}$)

| 1 | 2 | 3 | 4 | 5 | 6 | 7 | 8 | 9 | 10 | 11 | 12 | 13 | 14 | 15 | 16 | 17 | 18 |
|---|---|---|---|---|---|---|---|---|----|----|----|----|----|----|----|----|----|
| H 65·3 | | | | | | | | | | | | | | | | | He 126 |
| Li 28·2 | Be 9·5 | | | | | | | | | | | B 5·9 | C 5·7 | N 95·8 | O 102·5 | F 101·4 | Ne 146·5 |
| Na 51·2 | Mg 32·7 | | | | | | | | | | | Al 28·3 | Si 18·9 | P 44 | S 31·9 | Cl 111·5 | Ar 154·6 |
| K 64·2 | Ca 41·6 | Sc 38 | Ti 30·5 | V 29·3 | Cr 23·8 | Mn 32·0 | Fe 27·2 | Co 30·0 | Ni 30·0 | Cu 33·3 | Zn 41·6 | Ga 41 | Ge 42 | As 35 | Se 42·4 | Br 76 | Kr 163·9 |
| Rb 76 | Sr 52 | Y 44 | Zr 39·0 | Nb 36·5 | Mo 28·6 | Tc | Ru 29 | Rh 32 | Pd 37·8 | Ag 42·7 | Cd 51·8 | In 58 | Sn 51·4 | Sb 45·7 | Te 49·7 | I 58·1 | Xe 170 |
| Cs 84·3 | Ba 67 | La 57 | Hf 45·6 | Ta 41·5 | W 33·5 | Re 37 | Os 33 | Ir 36 | Pt 41·6 | Au 47·4 | Hg 76·0 | Tl 64·2 | Pb 64·8 | Bi 56 | Po | At | Rn 176 |
| Fr | Ra | Ac | | | | | | | | | | | | | | | |
| | | | Th 53·4 | Pa | U 50·3 | | | | | | | | | | | | |

Data from G. N. Lewis and M. Randall (1961), and O. Kubaschewski, E. L. Evans and C.B. Alcock (1967).

**Table 26** Entropy Contributions in Solid Compounds at 298 K, $S/(\text{J K}^{-1} \text{ mol}^{-1})$

*of metals*

| Li | Be | | | | | | | | | | | | | |
|----|----|---|---|---|---|---|---|---|---|---|---|---|---|---|
| 15 | 18 | | | | | | | | | | | | | |
| Na | Mg | Al | | | | | | | | | | | | |
| 31 | 32 | 33 | | | | | | | | | | | | |
| K  | Ca | Sc | Ti | V  | Cr | Mn | Fe | Co | Ni | Cu | Zn | Ga | Ge | As |
| 38 | 39 | 41 | 41 | 42 | 43 | 43 | 44 | 44 | 44 | 45 | 46 | 47 | 47 | 47·9 |
| Rb | Sr | Y  | Zr | Nb | Mo | Tc | Ru | Rh | Pd | Ag | Cd | In | Sn | Sb |
| 50 | 50 | 50 | 51 | 51 | 51 | 52 | 52 | 52 | 53 | 54 | 54 | 54 | 55 | 55 |
| Cs | Ba | La | Hf | Ta | W  | Re | Os | Ir | Pt | Au | Hg | Tl | Pb | Bi |
| 57 | 57 | 58 | 62 | 62 | 63 | 63 | 63 | 64 | 64 | 64 | 64 | 64 | 65 | 65 |

*of negative ions*

| | Charge on cation | | | |
|---|---|---|---|---|
| | 1+ | 2+ | 3+ | 4+ |
| $F^-$ | 23 | 20 | 17 | 21 |
| $Cl^-$ | 42 | 34 | 29 | 34 |
| $Br^-$ | 54 | 46 | 38 | 42 |
| I | 61 | 57 | 52 | 54 |
| $O^{2-}$ | 10 | 2 | 2 | 4 |
| $S^{2-}$ | 34 | 21 | 5 | 10 |
| $Se^{2-}$ | 67 | 48 | 33 | |
| $Te^{2-}$ | 69 | 51 | 38 | |
| $OH^-$ | 21 | 19 | 13 | |
| $CN^-$ | 30 | 25 | | |
| $NO_2^-$ | 74 | 63 | | |
| $NO_3^-$ | 91 | 74 | 63 | 59 |
| $CO_3^{2-}$ | 64 | 48 | 33 | |
| $HCO_3^-$ | 73 | 54 | 42 | |
| $C_2O_4^{2-}$ | 92 | 74 | 59 | |
| $ClO_3^-$ | 104 | 84 | | |
| $ClO_4^-$ | 109 | 92 | | |
| $BrO_3^-$ | 111 | 96 | 79 | |
| $IO_3^-$ | 107 | 92 | | |
| $MnO_4^-$ | 133 | 117 | | |
| $SO_3^{2-}$ | 79 | 62 | 46 | |
| $SO_4^{2-}$ | 92 | 72 | 57 | 50 |
| $CrO_4^{2-}$ | 110 | 88 | | |
| $PO_4^{3-}$ | 100 | 71 | 50 | |

Data based on those of W. M. Latimer (1952).

**100    Energetics of Ionic Crystals**

For this purpose it is necessary to estimate the radius of the unknown cation $Cs^{2+}$. This ion is likely to be smaller than the unipositive species $Cs^+$ ($r_{Pauling} = 0.169$ nm) but larger than the ion $Ba^{2+}$ ($r_{Pauling} = 0.135$ nm) in which the nuclear charge is one unit higher. Using $r_{Pauling} = 0.136$ nm for the fluoride ion $F^-$, the internuclear distance $r_c + r_a$ lies somewhere within the limits $0.305$–$0.271$ nm, and the lattice energy, from Kapustinskii's second equation, within the range $-2117$ to $-2414$ kJ mol$^{-1}$. If it is hoped to prepare $CsF_2$, one may take the optimistic view that the lattice energy (and because of the approximations involved, the lattice enthalpy also) will lie at the higher end of this range. Hence

$$\Delta H_f^\circ, CsF_2(s) = \Delta H_f^\circ, Cs^{2+}(g) + \Delta H_f^\circ, 2F^-(g) + \Delta H_{lattice}^\circ$$

$$= 2874 - 519 - 2414$$

$$= -59 \text{ kJ mol}^{-1}.$$

$\Delta S_f^\circ, CsF_2(s):$

The entropy $S_{298}^\circ$ for $CsF_2$ can be assessed roughly from Latimer's (Table 26) values for Cs (57 J K$^{-1}$ mol$^{-1}$) and $F^-$(20 J K$^{-1}$ mol$^{-1}$ in a salt $MF_2$), whence $S_{298}^\circ, CsF_2(s) = 57 + 40 = 97$ J K$^{-1}$ mol$^{-1}$, and

$$\Delta S_f^\circ = S_{298}^\circ, CsF_2(s) - S_{298}^\circ, Cs(s) - S_{298}^\circ, F_2(g)$$

$$= 97 - 84 - 203$$

$$= -190 \text{ J K}^{-1} \text{ mol}^{-1},$$

so that $\Delta G_f^\circ = \Delta H_f^\circ - T \Delta S_f^\circ$

$$= -59 - \left( \frac{298 (-190)}{1000} \right)$$

$$= -2 \text{ kJ mol}^{-1}.$$

The entropy change for the reaction is negative and unfavourable, mainly because of the entropy loss associated with the conversion of gaseous fluorine into a component of an ordered crystalline compound. It thus appears that, at best, the free energy of formation of $CsF_2$ might be barely negative. Moreover the free energy change for the disproportionation reaction

$$CsF_2(s) \rightarrow CsF(s) + \tfrac{1}{2}F_2(g)$$

is $-500 - (-2) = -498$ kJ mol$^{-1}$, indicating that the thermodynamic stability of $CsF_2$ with respect to the lower fluoride and fluorine gas is very low.

# Chapter 4
# Energetics of Covalent Compounds

## 4.1 Bond energies

In the preceding chapter it was seen that the structures of certain compounds can be conveniently represented as non-molecular assemblages of oppositely charged ions. In other cases, such an ionic model is unacceptable, either because the ions postulated would be chemically improbable (for example, $Si^{4+}C^{4-}$ as the components of silicon carbide) or because the properties of the substance are consistent with the presence of *molecular* units; the compound in such cases is described as predominantly *covalent*.

In the case of ionic substances, the energy quantity of primary interest is the energy change for the separation of the ions in the crystalline lattice into ions in the gas phase, that is the *lattice energy*.

Thus for sodium chloride, $\Delta U_0$ for the process

$$NaCl(s) \rightarrow Na^+(g) + Cl^-(g)$$

is $766 \text{ kJ mol}^{-1}$, and is a measure of the strength of the predominantly ionic bonds in the crystal. $\Delta U_0$ represents the amount by which the energy of one mole of $Na^+(g)$ ions and one mole of $Cl^-(g)$ ions, in the ideal gas state and lacking translational or rotational energies, is greater than the energy of one mole of crystalline NaCl, possessing only the zero-point vibration energy. If the zero-point energy (for NaCl, $7 \text{ kJ mol}^{-1}$) is added to $\Delta U_0$, the result ($773 \text{ kJ mol}^{-1}$) represents the 'pure' binding energy in the crystal, in that it is free of any vibrational energy contribution whatsoever. The room-temperature enthalpy change $\Delta H_{298}$ for the same process differs from $\Delta U_0$ in that it incorporates a small $P \Delta V$ term together with the small difference between the translational energy of the gaseous ions $Na^+(g)$ and $Cl^-(g)$, and the vibrational energy of the crystal sodium chloride. Thus $\Delta H_{298}$ is not as 'pure' a measure of bond strength as $\Delta U_0$, but the difference between the two quantities is commonly very small, and lattice enthalpies deduced from 298 K Born–Haber cycles are freely used as measures of ionic bond strength.

Turning now to covalent compounds, the corresponding quantity of theoretical interest is the energy change for the dissociation of the basic structural unit (commonly the *molecule*) into its component *atoms*, in the ideal gas state. In the course of dissociating in this way, the covalent *bonds* within the molecules are broken, and the energies involved are therefore known as bond energies. The general term 'bond energy' is, however, one which must be examined closely.

### 4.1.1 Bond-dissociation energy D

For a diatomic molecule such as $H_2$, the change in internal energy $\Delta U_0$ at 0 K for the dissociation

$$H_2(g) \rightarrow 2H(g),$$

where the reactant molecules and product atoms are in their ground states, is called the *bond-dissociation energy, D*. As discussed in section 1.2.4, it represents the amount by which the internal energy of two moles of hydrogen atoms (without translational, rotational or vibrational energy) is greater than the internal energy of one mole of hydrogen molecules (without translational or rotational energy, and possessing only the zero-point vibrational energy); $\Delta U_0 = 432\ \mathrm{kJ\ (mol\ H_2)}^{-1}$. If the zero-point energy ($26\ \mathrm{kJ\ mol^{-1}}$) is added to $\Delta U_0$, the result ($458\ \mathrm{kJ\ mol^{-1}}$) is the energy increase for the hypothetical dissociation $H_2 \rightarrow 2H$ in which all forms of thermal energy, and the zero-point energy as well, are absent in both reactants and products. The quantity $458\ \mathrm{kJ\ mol^{-1}}$ is therefore a 'pure' bond energy, in that it is the measure solely of the electrostatic interactions which distinguish the $H_2$ molecule from its component atoms. It is usual, however, to use the term 'bond-dissociation energy' to describe $\Delta U_0$ itself.

For polyatomic molecules, there will be more than one bond-dissociation energy $D$. Thus for ammonia,

$$NH_3(g) \rightarrow NH_2(g) + H(g) \qquad \Delta U_0 = D_1 = 448\ \mathrm{kJ\ mol^{-1}},$$
$$NH_2(g) \rightarrow NH(g) + H(g) \qquad \Delta U_0 = D_2 = 368\ \mathrm{kJ\ mol^{-1}},$$
$$NH(g) \rightarrow N(g) + H(g) \qquad \Delta U_0 = D_3 = 356\ \mathrm{kJ\ mol^{-1}},$$

and for water,

$$H_2O(g) \rightarrow OH(g) + H(g) \qquad \Delta U_0 = D_1 = 497\ \mathrm{kJ\ mol^{-1}},$$
$$OH(g) \rightarrow O(g) + H(g) \qquad \Delta U_0 = D_2 = 421\ \mathrm{kJ\ mol^{-1}}.$$

It is clear from these data that the dissociation energy of a bond between two specified atoms (e.g. N and H) is not a constant quantity, and that its value depends on the molecular environment of the atoms considered. It is necessary therefore to specify the bond involved in the symbol used,

e.g. $D_{H_2N-H} = 448\ \mathrm{kJ\ mol^{-1}}$.

Sometimes $\Delta H_{298}$ is measured instead of $\Delta U_0$; the difference between the two quantities (discussed in section 1.3.1) is usually not very great,

e.g. $Cl_2(g) \rightarrow 2Cl(g)$
$$\Delta U_0 = 239\ \mathrm{kJ\ mol^{-1}} \qquad \Delta H_{298} = 242\ \mathrm{kJ\ mol^{-1}}.$$

### 4.1.2 *Thermochemical bond energy E*

For many chemical purposes it is convenient to have a measure of the *average* value of the energy of a particular bond. For example, an average N—H bond energy derived from the enthalpy of atomization of ammonia,

$$NH_3(g) \rightarrow N(g) + 3H(g) \qquad \Delta H_{298} = 1172 \text{ kJ mol}^{-1},$$

is one third of $1172 = 391 \text{ kJ mol}^{-1}$.

This result is called the *thermochemical bond energy* (or simply the *bond energy*) $E_{N-H}$, of the N—H bond.

A problem arises in cases where a molecule contains more than one sort of bond, for example hydrazine,

which contains four N—H bonds and one N—N bond.

**Table 27** Mean Thermochemical Bond Energies, $E_{A-B}/(\text{kJ mol}^{-1})$

**X—X** *bonds*

| H—H | C—C | N—N | O—O | F—F |
|---|---|---|---|---|
| (H₂) | (diamond) | (H₂N.NH₂) | (H₂O₂) | (F₂) |
| 436 | 356 | 160* | 146* | 158 |
| | Si—Si | P—P | S—S | Cl—Cl |
| | (silicon) | (P₄) | (S₈) | (Cl₂) |
| | 226 | 209 | 226 | 242 |
| | Ge—Ge | | Se—Se | Br—Br |
| | (germanium) | | (Se₆) | (Br₂) |
| | 188 | | 172 | 193 |
| | Sn—Sn | | | I—I |
| | (grey tin) | | | (I₂) |
| | 151 | | | 151 |

**X—H** *bonds*

| C—H | N—H | O—H | F—H |
|---|---|---|---|
| (CH₄) | (NH₃) | (H₂O) | (HF) |
| 416 | 391 | 467 | 566 |
| Si—H | P—H | S—H | Cl—H |
| (SiH₄) | (PH₃) | (H₂S) | (HCl) |
| 323 | 322 | 347 | 431 |
| Ge—H | As—H | Se—H | Br—H |
| (GeH₄) | (AsH₃) | (H₂Se) | (HBr) |
| 289 | 247 | 276 | 366 |

| | | | | |
|---|---|---|---|---|
| Sn—H<br>($SnH_4$)<br>251 | | Te—H<br>($H_2Te$)<br>238 | I—H<br>(HI)<br>299 | |

X—C *bonds*

| | | | | |
|---|---|---|---|---|
| C—B<br>($BMe_3$)<br>372* | C—C<br>(diamond)<br>356 | C—N<br>($MeNH_2$)<br>285* | C—O<br>(MeOH)<br>336* | C—F<br>($CF_4$)<br>485 |
| C—Al<br>($AlMe_3$)<br>255* | C—Si<br>($SiMe_4$)<br>301* | C—P<br>($PMe_3$)<br>264* | C—S<br>(EtSH)<br>272* | C—Cl<br>($CCl_4$)<br>327 |
| | C—Ge<br>($GeMe_4$)<br>255* | C—As<br>($AsMe_3$)<br>201* | C—Se<br>($SeEt_2$)<br>243* | C—Br<br>(EtBr)<br>285* |
| | C—Sn<br>($SnEt_4$)<br>226* | C—Sb<br>($SbMe_3$)<br>197* | | C—I<br>(MeI)<br>213* |
| | C—Pb<br>($PbMe_4$)<br>130* | C—Bi<br>($BiMe_3$)<br>130* | | |
| C—Zn<br>($ZnMe_2$)<br>167* | C—Cd<br>($CdMe_2$)<br>134* | C—Hg<br>($HgMe_2$)<br>113* | | |

X—*halogen bonds*

| | | | |
|---|---|---|---|
| B—F<br>($BF_3$)<br>644 | B—Cl<br>($BCl_3$)<br>444 | B—Br<br>($BBr_3$)<br>368 | B—I<br>($BI_3$)<br>272 |
| Si—F<br>($SiF_4$)<br>582 | Si—Cl<br>($SiCl_4$)<br>391 | Si—Br<br>($SiBr_4$)<br>310 | Si—I<br>($SiI_4$)<br>234 |
| | Ge—Cl<br>($GeCl_4$)<br>342 | Ge—Br<br>($GeBr_4$)<br>276 | Ge—I<br>($GeI_4$)<br>213 |
| | Sn—Cl<br>($SnCl_4$)<br>320 | Sn—Br<br>($SnBr_4$)<br>272 | |
| | Pb—Cl<br>($PbCl_4$)<br>244 | | |

**Table 27**—*continued*

**Table 27**—*continued*

X—*halogen bonds* (*continued*)

| N—F | N—Cl | | |
|---|---|---|---|
| $(NF_3)$ | $(NCl_3)$ | | |
| 272 | 193 | | |
| P—F | P—Cl | P—Br | P—I |
| $(PF_3)$ | $(PCl_3)$ | $(PBr_3)$ | $(PI_3)$ |
| 490 | 319 | 264 | 184 |
| As—F | As—Cl | As—Br | As—I |
| $(AsF_3)$ | $(AsCl_3)$ | $(AsBr_3)$ | $(AsI_3)$ |
| 464 | 317 | 243 | 180 |
| | Sb—Cl | | |
| | $(SbCl_3)$ | | |
| | 312 | | |
| | Bi—Cl | | |
| | $(BiCl_3)$ | | |
| | 280 | | |
| O—F | O—Cl | | |
| $(F_2O)$ | $(Cl_2O)$ | | |
| 190 | 205 | | |
| S—F | S—Cl | | |
| $(SF_6)$ | $(S_2Cl_2)$ | | |
| 326 | 255* | | |
| Se—F | Se—Cl | | |
| $(SeF_6)$ | $(SeCl_2)$ | | |
| 285 | 243 | | |
| Te—F | | | |
| $(TeF_6)$ | | | |
| 335 | | | |

*Multiple bonds* (Single bond energies are shown for comparison)

| | C—C | N—N | O—O |
|---|---|---|---|
| | $(C_2H_6)$ | $(N_2H_4)$ | $(H_2O_2)$ |
| | 346* | 160* | 146* |
| | C=C | N=N | "O=O" |
| | $(C_2H_4)$ | $(C_6H_{14}N_2)$ | $(O_2)$ |
| | 598* | 418* | 498 |
| | C≡C | N≡N | |
| | $(C_2H_2)$ | $(N_2)$ | |
| | 813* | 946 | |

|  |  |
|---|---|
| P—P | S—S |
| (P$_4$) | (S$_8$) |
| 209 | 226 |
| P≡P | "S≡S" |
| (P$_2$) | (S$_2$) |
| 489 | 427 |

|  |  |
|---|---|
| C—N | C—O |
| (MeNH$_2$) | (MeOH) |
| 285* | 336* |
| C≡N | C≡O |
| (HCN) | (HCHO) |
| 866* | 695* |

The experimental heat of atomization of hydrazine, viz $\Delta H_{298}$ for the reaction

$$N_2H_4(g) \rightarrow 2N(g) + 4H(g),$$

is known and is equal to 1724 kJ mol$^{-1}$. This is the enthalpy change which occurs when four N—H bonds and one N—N bond are broken. Is it possible to assign a proportion of $\Delta H_{298}$ for the total atomization process to each of the bonds? This can be done, but only in a rather arbitrary way. It may be assumed, for example, that $\Delta H_{298}$ for the fission of the four N—H bonds is four times $E_{N-H}$ for the NH$_3$ molecule, viz $4 \times 391 = 1564$ kJ mol$^{-1}$, and that $\Delta H_{298}$ for the fission of the N—N bond is thus $1724 - 1564 = 160$ kJ mol$^{-1}$. This is in fact the only technique for assigning a value to $E_{N-N}$, since there is no molecule – for example, a nitrogen analogue (N$_4$) of white phosphorus – which contains *only* N—N single bonds. Many bond energies must be obtained in this indirect way.

Some thermochemical bond energies are listed in Table 27. The substances from whose heat of atomization the $E$ value was derived are also shown. Values of $E$ which are 'secondary' in the sense that they depend on an assumed energy for other bonds present in the molecule under consideration are marked with an asterisk.

The extent to which bond energies may be summed to give a value for the heat of atomization of a molecule for which thermochemical data are lacking is discussed in section 4.5.2.

## 4.2    Factors contributing to bond energies

It has been established in the foregoing discussion that the individual bond energies for the stepwise dissociation of a molecule – for example $D_{H_2N-H}$

$D_{\text{HN-H}}$ and $D_{\text{N-H}}$ – are not necessarily the same, and it will be seen in section 4.5.2 that the mean thermochemical bond energies for molecules in which the central atom exhibits different oxidation states – for example $PCl_3$ and $PCl_5$ – may also be different. The possible reasons for these departures from constancy can be appreciated by considering the factors which contribute to the energy changes which occur when bonds are formed or broken.

Consider for example the group 4 elements carbon, silicon, germanium, tin and lead, which form tetravalent compounds $MX_4$ such as halides and hydrides. The total bond-formation process

$$M(g) + 4X(g) \rightarrow MX_4(g),$$

where   $M = C, Si, Ge, Sn, Pb$

and   $X = H, F, Cl,$

involves the combination of gas-phase atoms in their ground states. In particular $M(g)$ is an atom whose valence-shell configuration is $ns^2 np_x^1 np_y^1$, that is the valence-shell comprises a pair of electrons occupying a spherically symmetrical $ns$ orbital, together with two unpaired electrons which occupy, singly, two of the $np$ orbitals. In order for such an atom to form four covalent bonds with hydrogen or halogen atoms, it is necessary first that the $ns$ electron pair be uncoupled and one electron of the pair promoted to the vacant $np_z$ orbital, giving an atom with four unpaired electrons and configuration $ns^1 np_x^1 np_y^1 np_z^1$. There is in general more than one spectroscopically identifiable stationary state corresponding to this configuration, but that of lowest energy is the stationary state with term symbol $^5S$, which in the case of carbon C lies at $3373 \cdot 5$ mm$^{-1}$ or 404 kJ mol$^{-1}$ above the ground ($^3P$) state, and in the case of silicon Si at $3332 \cdot 6$ mm$^{-1}$ or 399 kJ mol$^{-1}$ above the ground state. The first step in the bond-formation process is thus the energy-absorbing transition

(i)   $M(s^2 p_x^1 p_y^1)(g) \rightarrow M^*(s^1 p_x^1 p_y^1 p_z^1)(g).$

In the product of this transition, however, the four unpaired electrons are distributed among three $p$-orbitals which are mutually at right angles, and one $s$-orbital which has no preferred spatial orientation. Since the product molecules $MX_4$ have tetrahedral symmetry, the next step in the bond-formation process may be envisaged as the energy-absorbing rearrangement of the orbitals of the excited $M^*$ atom to produce an atom in its 'valence state' a state in which the orbitals have the correct spatial distribution (i.e. tetrahedral $sp^3$ hybrids), and the electrons in them are free of any interactions involving their spins or orbital motions:

(ii)   $M^*(s^1 p_x^1 p_y^1 p_z^1)(g) \rightarrow M_{vs}^*(sp^3 \text{ hybrids}) (g).$

The resulting state is *not* a stationary state of the atom, that is it is not observable spectroscopically, and hence the excitation energy involved cannot be determined experimentally – nor can it be rigorously calculated, but approximate values have been obtained from weighted averages of empirical promotion energies.

The final step is the energy-releasing combination of the 'prepared' atom $M_{vs}^*$ with the atoms $4X(g)$ (which may also have been involved in suitable preliminary excitation processes) to give the product molecule $MX_4(g)$:

(iii)   $M_{vs}^*(g) + 4X(g) \rightarrow MX_4(g)$.

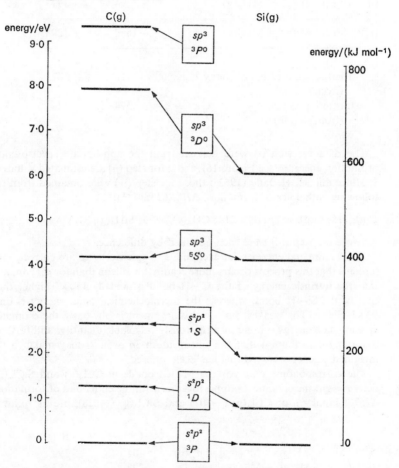

Figure 16 Spectroscopic energy levels of C(g) and Si(g) atoms. The energies necessary to excite an electron from the ground state $s^2p^2$ configuration ($^3P$) to the lowest-lying $sp^3$ configuration ($^5S$) are C: 4·18 eV or 404 kJ mol$^{-1}$ and Si: 4·13 eV or 399 kJ mol$^{-1}$.

**109   Factors Contributing to Bond Energies**

It is in this final step that the bonds are actually formed, and the energy released thereby has been called the 'intrinsic bond energy'.

The contributions, $\Delta H_{298}/(\text{kJ mol}^{-1})$, of steps (i, ii and iii) above for the M—H bonds in $CH_4$ and $SiH_4$ are as follows:

|  |  | C | Si |
|---|---|---|---|
| (i) | $M(s^2 p_x^1 p_y^1)(g) \rightarrow M^*(s^1 p_x^1 p_y^1 p_z^1)(g)$ | 404 | 399 |
| (ii) | $M^*(g) \rightarrow M_{vs}^*(g)$ | 228 | 85 |
| (iii) | $M_{vs}^*(g) + 4H(g) \rightarrow MH_4(g)$ | $-2294$ | $-1777$ |
| (iv) | $M(g) + 4H(g) \rightarrow MH_4(g)$ | $-1662$ | $-1293$ |
| | Thermochemical bond energy $E_{\text{M-H}}$ (from step iv) | 416 | 323 |
| | Intrinsic bond energy (from step iii) | 574 | 444 |

The data for step (i) were derived from the appropriate spectroscopic promotion energies (see Figure 16); those for step (ii) are estimated values of J. Hinze and H. H. Jaffé (1962); those for step (iv) were obtained from the following enthalpies of formation, $\Delta H_f^\circ/(\text{kJ mol}^{-1})$:

C(g), 715; Si(g), 452; H(g), 218; $CH_4$(g), $-75$; $SiH_4$(g), 31.

Those for step (iii) were then obtained by difference.

If the estimated energies for excitations to valence states are correct, then it seems that this process occurs more readily for silicon than for carbon, and that the intrinsic energy of the C—H bond is actually 130 kJ higher than that of the Si—H bond, whereas the thermochemical bond energy is only 93 kJ higher. The weakest link in this argument is obviously the estimated valence state energy – it is not a rigorously calculable quantity, and furthermore any contribution that the silicon atom $3d$ orbitals may make to the imagined valence state hybrids has been ignored.

The corresponding data for the M—Cl bonds in $CCl_4$(g) and $SiCl_4$(g), derived as in the previous example together with the enthalpies of formation, $\Delta H_f^\circ/(\text{kJ mol}^{-1})$, of $CCl_4$(g) ($-107$) and $SiCl_4$(g) ($-628$), are as follows:

|  |  | C | Si |
|---|---|---|---|
| (i) | $M(s^2 p_x^1 p_y^1)(g) \rightarrow M^*(s^1 p_x^1 p_y^1 p_z^1)(g)$ | 404 | 399 |
| (ii) | $M^*(g) \rightarrow M_{vs}^*(g)$ | 228 | 85 |
| (iii) | $M_{vs}^*(g) + 4Cl(g) \rightarrow MCl_4(g)$ | $-1938$ | $-2048$ |
| (iv) | $M(g) + 4Cl(g) \rightarrow MCl_4(g)$ | $-1306$ | $-1564$ |

| Thermochemical bond energy, $E_{M-Cl}$ (from step iv) | 327 | 391 |
|---|---|---|
| Intrinsic bond energy (from step iii) | 485 | 512 |

In this case the bonds formed by silicon are *stronger* than those formed by carbon, although in the case of the intrinsic energies the difference is numerically smaller. This treatment has neglected (a) any possible contribution of $3d$ orbitals to the 'valence state' of silicon, (b) the possibility of multiple bonding in $SiCl_4$, arising from the interaction of chlorine-atom lone electron pairs with vacant silicon-atom $3d$ orbitals, and (c) the possibility that the chlorine atoms may require excitation as a preliminary to bond formation; in its ground state, the chlorine atom has a singly occupied $p$-orbital available, but it is at least conceivable that the bond-forming orbital contains a proportion of $s$-character, and that an appropriate promotion energy is involved in constructing such an orbital.

These considerations illustrate the complexity of the bond formation process, and emphasize the absence of any suitable technique, based either on experimental data or rigorously applicable theory, for analysing the total bond energy into its component parts. Predictions of the total bond energy for a particular covalent molecule must therefore rely largely on mean values of experimentally determined bond energies. In the case of ionic compounds the situation is rather more satisfactory, in that the problem of predicting binding or lattice energies can usually be tackled theoretically with a fair chance of success.

## 4.3 Periodic trends in $\Delta G_f^\circ$ and $\Delta H_f^\circ$ for covalent compounds

In this section the factors responsible for the *trends* in the free energies and enthalpies of formation of covalent compounds are examined. It is difficult to generalize in a field as extensive as this, and the following three examples have been chosen to illustrate the problems which arise.

### 4.3.1 *The gaseous hydrogen halides*, HX (X = F, Cl, Br, I)

The enthalpies and free energies of formation of the gaseous hydrogen halides at 298 K are as follows:

|  | HF | HCl | HBr | HI |
|---|---|---|---|---|
| $\Delta H_f^\circ/(\text{kJ mol}^{-1})$ | −269 | −92·3 | −36·2 | +26 |
| $\Delta G_f^\circ/(\text{kJ mol}^{-1})$ | −271 | −95·3 | −53·2 | +1·3 |

Both $\Delta H_f^\circ$ and $\Delta G_f^\circ$ become less negative in passing along the series from HF to HI; in the case of hydrogen iodide both quantities are actually positive. The contributions of the entropy term $T \Delta S$ are as follows:

| | HF | HCl | HBr | HI |
|---|---|---|---|---|
| $T \Delta S_f^{\circ}/(\text{kJ mol}^{-1})$ | $+2$ | $+3 \cdot 0$ | $+17 \cdot 0$ | $+24 \cdot 6$ |
| $(T = 298 \cdot 2 \text{ K})$ | | | | |

In the case of HF and HCl the entropy contribution is very small. As discussed in section 1.4.3, $\Delta S_{298}^{\circ}$ for a gaseous reaction in which there is no change in the number of gas molecules is always close to zero, and all the species involved in the formation reaction

$$\tfrac{1}{2}H_2(g) + \tfrac{1}{2}X_2(\text{s.s.}) \rightarrow HX(g)$$

are gaseous when $X = F$ and Cl.

However, when $X = Br$, the element is a *liquid* in its standard state, and when $X = I$ the element is a *solid*, so that the formation reaction involves a net *increase* in the number of gas molecules and a significant positive value of $\Delta S_f^{\circ}$.

The factors responsible for the trend in $\Delta H_f^{\circ}$ can be ascertained from the following reaction sequence:

| | | HF | HCl | HBr | HI |
|---|---|---|---|---|---|
| (i) | $\tfrac{1}{2}H_2(g) \rightarrow H(g)$ | $+217 \cdot 9$ | $+217 \cdot 9$ | $+217 \cdot 9$ | $+217 \cdot 9$ |
| (ii) | $\tfrac{1}{2}X_2(\text{s.s.}) \rightarrow \tfrac{1}{2}X_2(g)$ | $0 \cdot 0$ | $0 \cdot 0$ | $+15 \cdot 6$ | $+31 \cdot 2$ |
| (iii) | $\tfrac{1}{2}X_2(g) \rightarrow X(g)$ | $+79$ | $+121 \cdot 1$ | $+96 \cdot 4$ | $+75 \cdot 6$ |
| (iv) | $\tfrac{1}{2}H_2(g) + \tfrac{1}{2}X_2(\text{s.s.})$ | | | | |
| | $H(g) \rightarrow + X(g)$ | $+297$ | $+339 \cdot 0$ | $+329\ 9$ | $+324 \cdot 7$ |
| (v) | $H(g) + X(g) \rightarrow HX(g)$ | $-566$ | $-431 \cdot 3$ | $-366 \cdot 1$ | $-299$ |
| (vi) | $\tfrac{1}{2}H_2(g) + \tfrac{1}{2}X_2(\text{s.s.}) \rightarrow HX(g)$ | $-269$ | $-92 \cdot 3$ | $-36 \cdot 2$ | $+26$ |
| | $= \Delta H_f^{\circ}/(\text{kJ mol}^{-1})$ | | | | |

The heat absorbed in the formation of gaseous atoms from the elements in their standard states – step (iv) – is not very much different for each halogen; noteworthy features are (a) the positive contributions of the heat of vaporization of $Br_2(l)$ and the heat of sublimation if $I_2(s)$, and (b) the low heat of atomization of $F_2(g)$. The dominating contribution to $\Delta H_f^{\circ}$ is made by the enthalpy change for step (v), that is by the thermochemical bond energy $E_{H-X}$, which decreases markedly from HF to HI. Hence the enthalpies of formation of the HX(g) molecules become substantially less negative in passing from HF to HI principally because of the decreasing covalent bond strength in the product molecules.

## 4.3.2 *The gaseous trichlorides*, $XCl_3$ (X = N, P, As, Sb, Bi)

The enthalpies and free energies of formation of the gaseous trichlorides

of the group nitrogen, phosphorus, arsenic, antimony and bismuth at 298 K
are as follows. The contribution of the entropy term $T \Delta S$ is also shown:

|  | $NCl_3$ | $PCl_3$ | $AsCl_3$ | $SbCl_3$ | $BiCl_3$ |
|---|---|---|---|---|---|
| $\Delta H_f^\circ/(kJ\ mol^{-1})$ | $+258$ | $-279$ | $-299$ | $-315$ | $-271$ |
| $\Delta G_f^\circ/(kJ\ mol^{-1})$ | $+298*$ | $-259$ | $-287$ | $-303$ | $-260$ |
| $T \Delta S_f^\circ/(kJ\ mol^{-1})$ | $-40$ | $-20$ | $-13$ | $-12$ | $-10$ |

*estimated by calculating $S_{298}^\circ$, $NCl_3(g)$ as approximately 297 J K$^{-1}$ mol$^{-1}$
(see section 4.5.4).

The most notable feature of these data is the high positive value of $\Delta H_f^\circ$
and $\Delta G_f^\circ$ for $NCl_3(g)$. For the other compounds, the values are all negative;
the trends from $PCl_3$ to $BiCl_3$ are irregular, the values of both $\Delta H_f^\circ$ and
$\Delta G_f^\circ$ becoming more negative from $PCl_3$ to $SbCl_3$ and then falling again at
$BiCl_3$. In all cases the entropy contribution ($T \Delta S_f^\circ$) to $\Delta G_f^\circ$ is small compared
to the enthalpy term, and is largest in the case of $NCl_3$. The fact that $T \Delta S_f^\circ$
for $NCl_3$ is about twice that for $PCl_3$ stems largely from the fact that elementary nitrogen in its standard state is a gas, whereas elementary phosphorus
is a solid; the individual entropies of the reactants and products in the formation reactions

$$\tfrac{1}{2}N_2(g) + 1\tfrac{1}{2}Cl_2(g) \rightarrow NCl_3(g)$$

$S_{298}^\circ$:   96        334            297,

$\Delta S_{298}^\circ = -133$ J K$^{-1}$ mol$^{-1}$

and     $P(s) + 1\tfrac{1}{2}Cl_2(g) \rightarrow PCl_3(g)$

$S_{298}^\circ$:   44    334        312,

$\Delta S_{298}^\circ = -66$ J K$^{-1}$ mol$^{-1}$

show clearly the effect of the large entropy of gaseous $N_2$ compared to the
smaller entropy of solid phosphorus.

The terms contributing to $\Delta H_f^\circ$ are evident from the following reaction
sequence:

|  |  | N | P | As | Sb | Bi |
|---|---|---|---|---|---|---|
| (i) | $X(s.s.) \rightarrow X(g)$ | $+473$ | $+315$ | $+287$ | $+259$ | $+207$ |
| (ii) | $1\tfrac{1}{2}Cl_2(g) \rightarrow 3Cl(g)$ | $+363$ | $+363$ | $+363$ | $+363$ | $+363$ |
| (iii) | $X(g) + 3Cl(g) \rightarrow XCl_3(g)$ | $-578$ | $-957$ | $-950$ | $-937$ | $-841$ |
| (iv) | $X(s.s.) + 1\tfrac{1}{2}Cl_2(g) \rightarrow XCl_3(g)$ | | | | | |
| | $= \Delta H_f^\circ/(kJ\ mol^{-1})$ | $+258$ | $-279$ | $-300$ | $-315$ | $-271$ |

It is clear from these data that the factors responsible for the positive value of $\Delta H_f^\circ$ for $NCl_3(g)$ are (a) the high heat of atomization of elementary nitrogen (which is related to the extraordinary strength of the triple bond in the $N_2$ molecule), and (b) the weakness of the covalent N—Cl bond in the molecule $NCl_3$. The thermochemical bond energies $E_{X-Cl}$ (one third of $\Delta H$ for step iii above) are:

| | N—Cl | P—Cl | As—Cl | Sb—Cl | Bi—Cl |
|---|---|---|---|---|---|
| $E_{X-Cl}/(kJ\ mol^{-1})$ | 193 | 319 | 317 | 312 | 280 |

Pauling has attributed the low value of $E_{N-Cl}$ to the absence of any 'ionic–covalent resonance' stabilization of the N—Cl bond because of the near-equivalence of the electronegativities of N and Cl.

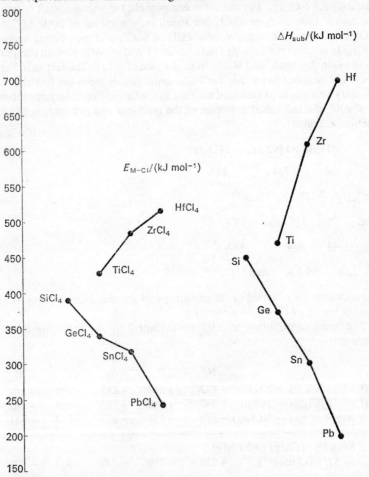

Figure 17  Sublimation enthalpies and thermochemical bond energies for Si, Ge, Sn, Pb, Ti, Zr, Hf, and their tetrachlorides.

4.3.3　*The gaseous tetrachlorides* $MCl_4$ (M = C, Si, Ge, Sn, Pb; Ti, Zr, Hf)

The enthalpies of formation of the gaseous tetrachlorides of the group 4 elements carbon, silicon, germanium, tin and lead, and of the transition elements titanium, zirconium and hafnium at 25°C are as follows:

|  | $CCl_4$ | $SiCl_4$ | $GeCl_4$ | $SnCl_4$ | $PbCl_4$ |
|---|---|---|---|---|---|
| $\Delta H_f^\circ/(kJ\ mol^{-1})$ | $-107$ | $-628$ | $-510$ | $-493$ | $-284$ |

|  | $TiCl_4$ | $ZrCl_4$ | $HfCl_4$ |
|---|---|---|---|
| $\Delta H_f^\circ/(kJ\ mol^{-1})$ | $-763$ | $-856$ | $-889$ |

The terms contributing to $\Delta H_f^\circ$ for the group 4 series are as follows:

|  |  | C | Si | Ge | Sn | Pb |
|---|---|---|---|---|---|---|
| (i) | $M(s.s.) \rightarrow M(g)$ | $+715$ | $+452$ | $+372$ | $+301$ | $+197$ |
| (ii) | $2Cl_2(g) \rightarrow 4Cl(g)$ | $+485$ | $+485$ | $+485$ | $+485$ | $+485$ |
| (iii) | $M(g)+4Cl(g) \rightarrow MCl_4(g)$ | $-1307$ | $-1565$ | $-1367$ | $-1279$ | $-974$ |
| (iv) | $M(s.s.)+2Cl_2(g) \rightarrow MCl_4(g)$ $= \Delta H_f^\circ/(kJ\ mol^{-1})$ | $-107$ | $-628$ | $-510$ | $-493$ | $-292$ |
| $E_{M-Cl}$: |  | 327 | 391 | 342 | 320 | 244 |

The enthalpies of formation of all five tetrachlorides are negative; the values increase from $PbCl_4$ to $SiCl_4$ and then fall sharply at $CCl_4$. The low value for $CCl_4$ is due in part to the high heat of sublimation of elementary carbon (step i) and in part to the fact that the C—Cl bond energy is not particularly high (it is lower than $E_{Si-Cl}$ and $E_{Ge-Cl}$). From silicon to lead the enthalpies of sublimation decrease steadily, but on the other hand the bond energies also decrease, the net effect of the two trends being to produce a decreasingly negative $\Delta H_f^\circ$.

It is interesting that the trends in the series $TiCl_4$, $ZrCl_4$ and $HfCl_4$ are in the reverse direction, as the following analysis demonstrates:

|  |  | Ti | Zr | Hf |
|---|---|---|---|---|
| (i) | $M(s) \rightarrow M(g)$ | $+473$ | $+611$ | $+703$ |
| (ii) | $2Cl_2(g) \rightarrow 4Cl(g)$ | $+485$ | $+485$ | $+485$ |
| (iii) | $M(g)+4Cl(g) \rightarrow MCl_4(g)$ | $-1721$ | $-1952$ | $-2077$ |
| (iv) | $M(s)+2Cl_2(g) \rightarrow MCl_4(g)$ $= \Delta H_f^\circ/(kJ\ mol^{-1})$ | $-763$ | $-856$ | $-889$ |
| $E_{M-Cl}$: |  | 430 | 488 | 519 |

In this group the sublimation enthalpies increase from titanium to hafnium, as do the bond energies; the balance is such as to make the formation reaction increasingly exothermic from titanium to hafnium. The trends in the series silicon, germanium, tin, lead and titanium, zirconium, hafnium are illustrated in Figure 17.

**Table 28**  Fusion and Vaporization Data for Molecular Substances

| | m.p./K | $\Delta H_{\text{fusion}}$ /(kJ mol⁻¹) at m.p. | $\Delta S_{\text{fusion}}$ /(J K⁻¹ mol⁻¹) at m.p. | b.p./K | $\Delta H_{\text{vap}}$ /(kJ mol⁻¹) at b.p. | $\Delta S_{\text{vap}}$ /(J K⁻¹ mol⁻¹) at b.p. |
|---|---|---|---|---|---|---|
| He | 3 | 0·02 | 7 | 4 | 0·08 | 21 |
| Ne | 24 | 0·33 | 14 | 27 | 1·76 | 65 |
| Ar | 84 | 1·18 | 14 | 87 | 6·5 | 75 |
| Kr | 116 | 1·64 | 14 | 120 | 9·0 | 75 |
| Xe | 161 | 2·30 | 14 | 165 | 12·6 | 77 |
| Rn | 202 | 2·67 | 13 | 211 | 16·4 | 78 |
| $H_2$ | 14 | 0·12 | 8 | 20 | 0·90 | 45 |
| $N_2$ | 63 | 0·72 | 11 | 77 | 5·57 | 72 |
| $O_2$ | 54 | 0·44 | 8 | 90 | 6·8 | 75 |
| HF | 190 | 3·9 | 21 | 292 | 32·6 | 112 |
| HCl | 159 | 2·0 | 13 | 188 | 16·2 | 86 |
| HBr | 186 | 2·4 | 13 | 206 | 17·6 | 85 |
| HI | 222 | 2·9 | 13 | 238 | 19·7 | 83 |
| $H_2S$ | 187 | 2·5 | 13 | 213 | 19 | 88 |
| $H_2Se$ | 207 | 2·5 | 12 | 232 | 19 | 83 |
| $P_4$ | 317 | 2·5 | 8 | 553 | 52 | 94 |
| $PH_3$ | 139 | 1·1 | 8 | 185 | 14·6 | 79 |
| $SiH_4$ | 88 | 0·7 | 8 | 161 | 13 | 77 |
| $CCl_4$ | 250 | 2·5 | 10 | 350 | 30·0 | 86 |
| $MoF_6$ | 290 | 4·4 | 15 | 309 | 25 | 81 |

| | | | | | | |
|---|---|---|---|---|---|---|
| $F_2$ | 53 | 1·6 | 30 | 85 | 6·3 | 74 |
| $Cl_2$ | 172 | 6·4 | 37 | 239 | 20·4 | 86 |
| $Br_2$ | 266 | 10·5 | 40 | 331 | 31·0 | 94 |
| $I_2$ | 387 | 15·8 | 40 | 456 | 41·7 | 91 |
| $PCl_3$ | 182 | 4·5 | 25 | 348 | 31 | 88 |
| $S_8$ | 392 | 10·0 | 26 | 763 | 63 | 83 |
| $SiCl_4$ | 203 | 7·7 | 38 | 330 | 28·7 | 87 |
| $GeCl_4$ | 223 | 7·7 | 34 | 356 | 30 | 83 |
| $SnCl_4$ | 240 | 9·2 | 38 | 387 | 34·9 | 86 |
| $TiCl_4$ | 250 | 9·4 | 38 | 410 | 36 | 88 |
| $HgCl_2$ | 550 | 18 | 32 | 577 | 59 | 102 |
| $BF_3$ | 144 | 4·2 | 29 | 172 | 19 | 112 |
| $AsF_3$ | 267 | 10·4 | 39 | 331 | 30 | 90 |
| $AsCl_3$ | 257 | 10 | 39 | 403 | 31 | 78 |
| $SO_2$ | 197 | 7·4 | 38 | 263 | 25 | 95 |
| $B_2H_6$ | 108 | 4·5 | 41 | 180 | 14·3 | 79 |
| $OsO_4$ | 313 | 14·3 | 46 | 403 | 39·5 | 98 |
| $Ni(CO)_4$ | 254 | 13·8 | 54 | 315 | 29 | 93 |
| $Fe(CO)_5$ | 252 | 13·6 | 54 | 378 | 37 | 99 |
| $Fe(CO)_2(NO)_2$ | 291 | 10·5 | 36 | 383 | 38·3 | 100 |
| $Fe(C_5H_5)_2$ | 459 | 23·0 | 50 | 522 | 47 | 96 |
| $Pb(CH_3)_4$ | 243 | 10·8 | 44 | 376 | 38·0 | 101 |

## 4.4    Melting points and boiling points of non-ionic crystals

The melting and boiling points of ionic crystals have been described in section 3.6, where a brief comparison with molecular crystals was also given. The latter class will now be discussed in more detail. Before doing so, however, it is worth noting that certain substances in which the bonding is predominantly *covalent* may have the same characteristically high melting points associated with ionic compounds – such substances are those in which individual molecules cannot be distinguished, and typical examples are those shown in the following tabulation:

|  | m.p./K |
|---|---|
| Silicon carbide, SiC | 3000* |
| Diamond | 3800 |
| Graphite | 3925* |
| Silicon dioxide, $SiO_2$ | 1986 |
| Boron nitride, BN | 3300* |

*sublimes

The fusion of such crystals must, of course, involve extensive disruption of the strong covalent bonds which extend throughout the crystal, and high temperatures are necessary to achieve this. Most predominantly covalent substances, however, form *molecular* crystals in which the strong covalent bonds are found only within small molecular units, which themselves are bound together by the much weaker van der Waals forces of attraction. These weak intermolecular forces constitute the points of structural weakness in such a crystal, and the temperature at which fusion occurs is usually low.

At the conventional melting and boiling points,

$$T/K \text{ (m.p.)} = \frac{\Delta H_{fusion}}{\Delta S_{fusion}} \quad \text{and} \quad T/K \text{ (b.p.)} = \frac{\Delta H_{vap}}{\Delta S_{vap}},$$

so that the actual melting point (or boiling point) is a constant to whose magnitude both an enthalpy and an entropy change contribute. The appropriate data for a number of representative molecular substances are shown in Table 28, and these will now be discussed.

### 4.4.1    *Melting points of molecular substances*

The lowest melting points are displayed by the noble gases (these are, of course, atomic rather than molecular substances), and are clearly a consequence of the small enthalpies of fusion. The entropy of fusion in each case (except for helium) is about $14 \text{ J K}^{-1} \text{ mol}^{-1}$, and it is noteworthy that entropies of fusion of about this magnitude are also observed for a number of diatomic and polyatomic molecules, for example, $H_2$, $N_2$, $O_2$, HCl, HBr, HI, $H_2S$, $H_2Se$, $P_4$, $PH_3$, $SiH_4$, $CCl_4$ and $MoF_6$. There are many molecular substances, however, whose entropies of fusion are distinctly higher – in the range

## 118 Energetics of Covalent Compounds

25–50 J K$^{-1}$ mol$^{-1}$, and it seems that the occurrence of 'low' entropies of fusion 8–12 J K$^{-1}$ mol$^{-1}$) may be associated with the fact that melting is preceded by solid-phase transitions involving entropy increases. For example, the melting of solid oxygen, $O_2$, at 54 K is preceded by two transitions in the solid:

| | |
|---|---|
| transition at 23·7 K | $\Delta S =$ 4 |
| transition at 43·8 K | 17 |
| fusion at 54·4 K | 8 |
| | — |
| | 29 J K$^{-1}$ mol$^{-1}$. |
| | — |

If the entropy changes are added, the total is 29 J K$^{-1}$ mol$^{-1}$. For a similar diatomic molecule such as $Cl_2$, however, there are no solid-phase transitions and the entire entropy increase (for $Cl_2$, 37 J K$^{-1}$ mol$^{-1}$) occurs when the solid melts.

The heats of fusion are difficult to systematize; their magnitudes depend heavily on the strengths of the intermolecular van der Waals forces in the solid, and the largest values of $\Delta H_{fusion}$ are observed for large, polarizable molecules like $I_2$ (15·8 kJ mol$^{-1}$) and $HgCl_2$ (18 kJ mol$^{-1}$).

### 4.4.2  *Boiling points of molecular substances*

Both the enthalpy and entropy changes which occur on vaporization of a liquid are considerably larger than the corresponding changes which accompany fusion; furthermore, the entropy of vaporization, except for substances with very low boiling points, is fairly constant within a range of about 80–95 J K$^{-1}$ mol$^{-1}$. A number of empirical rules depend on this rough constancy: for example Trouton's rule states that

$$\frac{\Delta H_{vap}}{\text{b.p.(K)}} \simeq 88 \text{ J K}^{-1} \text{ mol}^{-1},$$

and may be used to assess the heat of vaporization of a non-associated molecular liquid if its boiling point is known. Because of the relative constancy of $\Delta S_{vap}$, the boiling point of a molecular substance is in effect largely determined by the magnitude of the heat of vaporization, that is by the strength of the intermolecular van der Waals forces which must be overcome for the liquid → gas transition to occur. For a coherent series such as the halogens $X_2$, $\Delta H_{vap}$ (see Table 28) increases with increase in the size and polarizability of the $X_2$ molecules. Since the variation in $\Delta S_{vap}$ is relatively smaller, the boiling points follow the trend in $\Delta H_{vap}$ and increase from $F_2$ to $I_2$.

An instructive comparison may be made with the hydrogen halides HX, for which the data are given in Table 28. It is clear that the heat of vaporization of liquid hydrogen fluoride (to the ideal, i.e. non-associated, gas) is

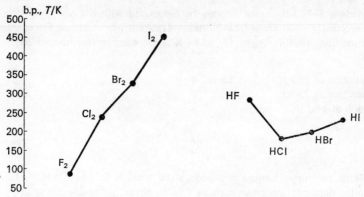

Figure 18 Boiling points of halogens and hydrogen halides

abnormally high, a consequence of the circumstance that in the liquid the intermolecular van der Waals forces are considerably reinforced by extensive HF $\cdots$ HF hydrogen bonding. That this hydrogen bonding in hydrogen fluoride also imposes restrictions on the translational freedom of the molecules in the liquid phase is evident from the significantly greater entropy of vaporization. The boiling point of liquid hydrogen fluoride is thus higher than that of any of the other hydrogen halides, which show the normal increase in boiling point from hydrogen chloride to hydrogen iodide. The trends in boiling points for the halogens and the hydrogen halides are shown in Figure 18.

Similar 'anomalously' high boiling points are shown by the first members of the two series $H_2O$, $H_2S$, $H_2Se$, $H_2Te$, and $NH_3$, $PH_3$, $AsH_3$, $SbH_3$.

An interesting example of structural influences on the enthalpy and entropy changes accompanying fusion and vaporization is seen in the following data for aluminium chloride and bromide:

|  | Aluminium chloride | Aluminium bromide |
| --- | --- | --- |
| m.p. | 463 K | 370 K |
| $\Delta H_{fusion}/\{kJ\ (mol\ AlX_3)^{-1}\}$ | 36 | 11 |
| $\Delta S_{fusion}/\{J\ K^{-1}\ (mol\ AlX_3)^{-1}\}$ | 77 | 31 |
| b.p. | 433 K | 528 K |
| $\Delta H_{vap}/\{kJ\ (mol\ AlX_3)^{-1}\}$ | 20·3 | 22·8 |
| $\Delta S_{vap}/\{J\ K^{-1}\ (mol\ AlX_3)^{-1}\}$ | 47 | 43 |

Each thermodynamic quantity is calculated for 133·3 g of aluminium chloride or 266·7 g of aluminium bromide, that is for one mole based on the formula weights of $AlCl_3$ and $AlBr_3$. On this basis. the entropies of vaporization are anomalously low. The explanation lies of course in the fact that both the chloride and the bromide form dimeric molecules in the liquid and vapour phases, so that the formula weight should be based on the unit $Al_2X_6$. The corrected entropies of vaporization then have the unexceptionable values 94 J K$^{-1}$ (mol Al$_2$Cl$_6$)$^{-1}$ and 86 J K$^{-1}$ (mol Al$_2$Br$_6$)$^{-1}$. The second notable feature of the data listed is the fact that both the enthalpy and the entropy of fusion of aluminium chloride are much higher than the corresponding quantities for aluminium bromide. This in turn stems from the fact that while aluminium bromide consists of Al$_2$Br$_6$ molecules in both the solid and liquid states, solid aluminium chloride has a layer lattice structure in which the aluminium has sixfold coordination. On melting, the layer lattice of the solid is transformed into a molecular liquid consisting of Al$_2$Cl$_6$ molecules in which the aluminium is involved in fourfold tetrahedral coordination. This more profound structural change is reflected in the high values of the enthalpy and entropy of fusion.

## 4.5 Estimation of $\Delta G_f^\circ$ for covalent compounds

This section follows the treatment of ionic compounds given in section 3.7.

### 4.5.1 Estimation of $\Delta H_f^\circ$

The critical part of any estimation of an enthalpy of formation is the evaluation of the binding energy. If the compound under consideration is described in terms of an ionic model, then the binding energy corresponds to the lattice energy. Where a covalent model is adopted, then the covalent bond energy is the quantity in question. For example, suppose it is desired to estimate $\Delta H_f^\circ$ for the hypothetical molecule

that is, $\Delta H^\circ_{298}$ for the reaction

$$\tfrac{1}{2}H_2(g) + 1\tfrac{1}{2}N_2(g) + 2Cl_2(g) \rightarrow HN_3Cl_4(l),$$

assuming that HN$_3$Cl$_4$ is a liquid in its standard state.

The appropriate sequence of reactions whose sum yields the formation reaction above is

| | | | sign |
|---|---|---|---|
| (i) | $\tfrac{1}{2}H_2(g) \rightarrow H(g)$ | $\Delta h_1$ | + |
| (ii) | $1\tfrac{1}{2}N_2(g) \rightarrow 3N(g)$ | $\Delta h_2$ | + |
| (iii) | $2Cl_2(g) \rightarrow 4Cl(g)$ | $\Delta h_3$ | + |
| (iv) | $H(g) + 3N(g) + 4Cl(g) \rightarrow HN_3Cl_4(g)$ | $\Delta h_4$ | − |
| (v) | $HN_3Cl_4(g) \rightarrow HN_3Cl_4(l)$ | $\Delta h_5$ | − |
| (vi) | $\tfrac{1}{2}H_2(g) + 1\tfrac{1}{2}N_2(g) + 2Cl_2(g) \rightarrow HN_3Cl_4(l)$ | $\Delta H_f^\circ$ | ? |

$\Delta h_1$, $\Delta h_2$, and $\Delta h_3$ (which are all positive) are the enthalpies of atomization of the elements from their standard states, and experimental values of these are given in Chapter 2, Table 10 (p. 46). The two reactions for which experimental values are, of course, not available are (iv), the formation of the gaseous molecule from its gaseous atoms, and (v), the condensation of the gaseous molecule to its standard (liquid) state. Thus $\Delta h_4$ is numerically equal to the total thermochemical bond energy for the molecule, and $\Delta h_5$ is the negative of its enthalpy of vaporization; both these enthalpy contributions must be estimated.

The enthalpy of vaporization of $HN_3Cl_4$ is likely to be quite small compared with the total bond energy, and a rough value is most easily obtained from known $\Delta H_{vap}$ data for molecules of similar size, shape and polarizability. Such a molecule is 1,1,3,3-tetrachloropropane,

$$\begin{array}{ccc}
Cl & CH_2 & Cl \\
\diagdown & \diagup \;\; \diagdown & \diagup \\
CH & & CH \\
| & & | \\
Cl & & Cl
\end{array}$$

for which the enthalpy of vaporization (estimated by Trouton's rule from its boiling point, 435 K) is approximately 38 kJ mol$^{-1}$. The corresponding quantity ($\Delta h_5$) for $HN_3Cl_4$ is unlikely to differ significantly from this; in any case an uncertainty of a few kilojoules in this quantity is small compared to the uncertainty in $\Delta h_4$ (the total bond energy) which it now remains to evaluate.

The usual procedure is to assume that the total enthalpy change for the bond-formation reaction (iv) can be divided into a number of contributions or terms representing the energies of the individual bonds.

Thus $\quad -\Delta h_4 = E_{total} = 2E_{N-N} + 4E_{N-Cl} + E_{N-H}$,

where $E$ is the enthalpy decrease accompanying the formation of the bond indicated, from its gaseous atoms. It is then assumed that each of these bond energy terms may be equated with the appropriate thermochemical bond energy listed in Table 27, that is it is assumed that bond energies are constant and additive. (The validity of this assumption is examined in section 4.5.2.)

Hence $\Delta h_4$ is given by

$$-\Delta h_4 = 2E_{N-N} + 4E_{N-Cl} + E_{N-H}$$

$$= (2 \times 160) + (4 \times 193) + 391$$

$$= 1483 \text{ kJ mol}^{-1}.$$

Since (from Table 10) $\Delta h_1 = 218$, $\Delta h_2 = 1418$, and $\Delta h_3 = 485$ kJ,

$$\Delta H_f^{\circ}, HN_3Cl_4(l) = \Delta h_1 + \Delta h_2 + \Delta h_3 + \Delta h_4 + \Delta h_5$$

$$= 218 + 1418 + 485 - 1483 - 38$$

$$= 600 \text{ kJ mol}^{-1}.$$

The compound is thus likely to be highly endothermic; a major cause of this is the high enthalpy of atomization of nitrogen ($\Delta h_2$), that is, the great strength of the N≡N triple bond relative to the bonds in the product.

### 4.5.2 *Constancy of bond energies*

It is clear from the above example that any estimation of a similar sort depends heavily on the accuracy with which the bond energy can be evaluated. There is no doubt that the energy of a particular bond will always depend to some degree on its molecular environment, and that the assumption of constancy from molecule to molecule introduces an element of uncertainty into any calculation which relies on tabulations of average bond energies. Unfortunately there is no general and straightforward way of making energetic corrections for the molecular environment of a bond, but it is often possible to recognize circumstances in which departures from constancy are likely to be marked.

For example, the energy $E$ of a bond A—B is unlikely to be constant for a series of compounds in which the oxidation states of A and B do not remain constant.

Thus a P—Cl bond energy can be derived from the following $\Delta H_f^\circ/(\text{kJ mol}^{-1})$ values:

$PCl_3(g)$, $-279$; $P(g)$, 315; $Cl(g)$, 121.

These yield $E_{\text{P-Cl}} = 319 \text{ kJ mol}^{-1}$

In the P(V) compound $PCl_5(g)$, however, for which $\Delta H_f^\circ = -371$ kJ mol$^{-1}$, the formation of the two additional P—Cl bonds in the process

$$PCl_3(g) + 2Cl(g) \rightarrow PCl_5(g)$$

evolves only 334 kJ mol$^{-1}$, so that the average energy of the two new bonds is only 167 kJ mol$^{-1}$, or little more than half of the average energy of the bonds in $PCl_3$.

Similarly, the following enthalpy data for the antimony chlorides, $\Delta H_f^\circ/(\text{kJ mol}^{-1})$,

$SbCl_3(g)$, $-315$; $SbCl_5(g)$, $-390$; $Sb(g)$, 259

yield $E_{\text{Sb-Cl}}$ in $SbCl_3 = 312 \text{ kJ mol}^{-1}$

and for the reaction

$$SbCl_3(g) + 2Cl(g) \rightarrow SbCl_5(g),$$

$\Delta H_{298}^\circ = -315$ kJ mol$^{-1}$, so that $E_{\text{Sb-Cl}}$ for the two additional bonds in $SbCl_5$ is only 158 kJ mol$^{-1}$, again little more than half the value of $E_{\text{Sb-Cl}}$ in $SbCl_3$.

Again, for the fluorides of iodine, the following enthalpy data, $\Delta H_f^\circ/(\text{kJ mol}^{-1})$,

IF(g), $-94$; IF$_5$(g), $-816$; IF$_7$(g), $-938$; I(g), $+107$, F(g), $+79$, permit the calculation of enthalpy changes for the reactions

$$\Delta H^\circ_{298}\ (\text{kJ mol}^{-1})$$

|      |                                       |        |
|------|---------------------------------------|--------|
| (i)  | $I(g) + F(g) \rightarrow IF(g)$       | $-280$ |
| (ii) | $IF(g) + 4F(g) \rightarrow IF_5(g)$   | $-1038$ |
| (iii)| $IF_5(g) + 2F(g) \rightarrow IF_7(g)$ | $-280$ |

from which it is clear that $E_{I-F}$ in iodine(I) fluoride is $280$ kJ mol$^{-1}$, but that the average energy of the four 'new' bonds formed in reaction (ii) in iodine(V) fluoride is $\frac{1}{4} \times 1038 = 260$ kJ mol$^{-1}$, while the average energy of the two 'new' bonds formed when iodine(VII) fluoride is produced in reaction (iii) is only $\frac{1}{2} \times 280 = 140$ kJ mol$^{-1}$. There is thus a decrease in the strength of the I—F bonds formed in the sequence

$$IF \rightarrow IF_5 \rightarrow IF\ .$$

Some thermochemical bond energies, $E/(\text{kJ mol}^{-1})$, for chlorine–metal bonds are as follows; the consistently lower value observed for the metal in its higher oxidation state is noteworthy:

| $E_{Ti-Cl}$ | $E_{Cr\ Cl}$ | $E_{Fe-Cl}$ | $E_{Sn-Br}$ |
|-------------|--------------|-------------|-------------|
| TiCl$_2$, 502 | CrCl$_2$, 381 | FeCl$_2$, 397 | SnBr$_2$, 326 |
| TiCl$_3$, 456 | CrCl$_3$, 356 | FeCl$_3$, 339 | SnBr$_4$, 272 |
| TiCl$_4$, 427 |              |             |             |

### 4.5.3 *Estimation of $\Delta H^\circ_f$ by Pauling's method*

One of the few attempts which have been made to systematize covalent bond energies is that of L. Pauling, who postulated that the observed decrease in bond energy along a series such as the following:

|                              | HF  | HCl | HBr | HI  |
|------------------------------|-----|-----|-----|-----|
| $E_{H-X}/(\text{kJ mol}^{-1})$ | 565 | 431 | 366 | 299 |

has its basis in the diminishing electronegativity difference between the bonded atoms. His suggestion is that for a single covalent bond between two atoms X and Y, the energy $E_{X-Y}$ of the bond X—Y is greater than the arithmetic mean of the single-bond energies $E_{X-X}$ and $E_{Y-Y}$ by an amount $\Delta$, which measures the extent to which the bond X—Y is stabilized by 'ionic–covalent resonance'.

Thus $\Delta = E'_{X-Y} - \frac{1}{2}(E_{X-X} + E_{Y-Y}).$  **4.1**

Electronegativity coefficients $\chi_X$ and $\chi_Y$ were next assigned to X and Y in such a way as to satisfy as far as possible the relationship

$$|\chi_X - \chi_Y| = \left(\frac{\Delta}{96}\right)^{\frac{1}{2}}.$$  **4.2**

**Table 29**  Electronegativity Coefficients (Pauling)

The coefficients are appropriate to the common oxidation states of the elements

| Li ·0 | Be 1·5 | B 2·0 | | | | | | | | | | C 2·5 | N 3·0 | O 3·5 | F 4·0 |
|---|---|---|---|---|---|---|---|---|---|---|---|---|---|---|---|
| Na 0·9 | Mg 1·2 | Al 1·5 | | | | | | | | | | Si 1·8 | P 2·1 | S 2·5 | Cl 3·0 |
| K 0·8 | Ca 1·0 | Sc 1·3 | Ti 1·5 | V 1·6 | Cr 1·6 | Mn 1·5 | Fe 1·8 | Co 1·8 | Ni 1·8 | Cu 1·9 | Zn 1·6 | Ga 1·6 | Ge 1·8 | As 2·0 | Se 2·4 | Br 2·8 |
| Rb 0·8 | Sr 1·0 | Y 1·2 | Zr 1·4 | Nb 1·6 | Mo 1·8 | Tc 1·9 | Ru 2·2 | Rh 2·2 | Pd 2·2 | Ag 1·9 | Cd 1·7 | In 1·7 | Sn 1·8 | Sb 1·9 | Te 2·1 | I 2·5 |
| Cs 0·7 | Ba 0·9 | La 1·1 | Hf 1·3 | Ta 1·5 | W 1·7 | Re 1·9 | Os 2·2 | Ir 2·2 | Pt 2·2 | Au 2·4 | Hg 1·9 | Tl 1·8 | Pb 1·8 | Bi 1·9 | Po 2·0 | At 2·2 |
| Fr 0·7 | Ra 0·9 | Ac 1·1 | Th 1·3 | Pa 1·5 | U 1·7 | | | | | | | | | | | |

The resulting coefficients are listed in Table 29.

It then follows from **4.1** and **4.2** above that

$$E_{X-Y} = \tfrac{1}{2}(E_{X-X} + E_{Y-Y}) + 96\,|\chi_X - \chi_Y|^2$$

and that, for a gaseous single-bonded molecule formed from gaseous single-bonded elements, the heat evolved would be approximately $96|\chi_X - \chi_Y|^2$ kJ mol$^{-1}$.

For example, $\Delta H^\circ_{298}$ for the reaction

$$\tfrac{1}{4}P_4(g) + 1\tfrac{1}{2}Br_2(g) \rightarrow PBr_3(g),$$

in which reactants and products are all single-bonded molecules, is $-3 \times 96|\chi_{Br} - \chi_P|^2$, which, with $\chi_{Br} = 2 \cdot 8$ and $\chi_P = 2 \cdot 1$, is $-141$ kJ (mol PBr$_3$(g))$^{-1}$. The experimental result is $-209$ kJ mol$^{-1}$.

If the reacting elements are not single-bonded gases, corrections must be made. Thus for NF$_3$, the quantity $3 \times 96|\chi_F - \chi_N|^2$, with $\chi_F = 4 \cdot 0$ and $\chi_N = 3 \cdot 0$, is 288 kJ (mol NF$_3$)$^{-1}$; however, in the reaction

$$\tfrac{1}{2}N_2(g) + 1\tfrac{1}{2}F_2(g) \rightarrow NF_3(g) \qquad\qquad \textbf{4.3}$$

elementary nitrogen consists not of single-bonded molecules but of triple-bonded N≡N molecules, in which the triple bond (N$_2$(g) → 2N(g), $\Delta H^\circ_{298} = 946$ kJ (mol N$_2$)$^{-1}$) is more stable than three N—N single bonds ($3E_{N-N} = 3 \times 160 = 480$ kJ) by $946 - 480 = 466$ kJ (mol N$_2$)$^{-1}$, or 233 kJ for half a mole of N$_2$; the expected enthalpy change for reaction **4.3** is thus $-(288 - 233) = -55$ kJ (mole NF$_3$)$^{-1}$. The experimental result is $-124$ kJ mol$^{-1}$.

Pauling's procedure produces results which are not very accurate, partly because of the inadequacy of his basic postulates, and partly because of difficulties in assigning satisfactory electronegativity coefficients to fit equation **4.2** above. It is useful, however, for obtaining rough measures of $\Delta H^\circ_f$ in cases where more accurate estimates cannot be made.

### 4.5.4 *Estimation of $\Delta S^\circ_f$*

In order to estimate $\Delta S^\circ_f$ for a covalent compound it is necessary to know the entropy $S^\circ_{298}$ of the compound itself, and also that of each constituent element in its standard state. The latter are tabulated in Table 25 (p. 99).

The estimation of $S^\circ_{298}$ for a molecular compound is best tackled empirically from observed trends for gaseous molecules. A plot of $S^\circ_{298}$ against molecular weight $M$ for known gaseous *polyatomic* molecules, using the data of Table 30, is shown in Figure 19, from which the entropies of new compounds can be obtained by interpolation with a fair degree of accuracy. Kubaschewski, Evans and Alcock (1967) have fitted empirical equations to curves such as these; their relationships are

(a) for diatomic gases other than hydrides,

$$S^\circ_{298} = 225 + 0 \cdot 18M - 1004M^{-1},$$

(b) for polyatomic gases of molecular weight not higher than 250,

$$S^\circ_{298} = 163 + 1 \cdot 4M - (2 \cdot 6 \times 10^{-3})M^2.$$

(This equation fails for molecular weights above 250.)

There appear to be certain classes of compound for which these empirical equations, and the empirical curve of Figure 19, are quite unsuitable. For example, the following gaseous carbonyls,

|  | $S^\circ_{298}/(\text{J K}^{-1}\,\text{mol}^{-1})$ | $M$ |
|---|---|---|
| $Fe(CO)_5$ | 444 | 195·9 |
| $Ni(CO)_4$ | 399 | 170·7 |
| $Cr(CO)_6$ | 487 | 220·0 |
| $Mo(CO)_6$ | 507 | 263·9 |

have exceptionally high entropies. The empirical relationships, however, seem to hold extensively for binary compounds.

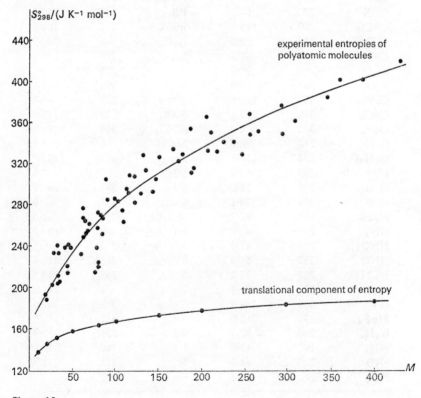

Figure 19

**Table 30** Entropy, $S_{298}^{\circ}/(\text{J K}^{-1}\,\text{mol}^{-1})$, and Molecular Weight, $M$, for Polyatomic Gaseous Molecules

| | $S_{298}^{\circ}$ | $M$ | | $S_{298}^{\circ}$ | $M$ |
|---|---|---|---|---|---|
| $AsCl_3$ | 327 | 181·3 | $N_2O_4$ | 304 | 92·0 |
| $AsF_3$ | 289 | 131·9 | $NF_3$ | 261 | 71·0 |
| $AsH_3$ | 223 | 77·9 | $NOF$ | 248 | 49·0 |
| $BBr_3$ | 324 | 250·6 | $NOCl$ | 264 | 65·5 |
| $BCl_3$ | 290 | 117·2 | $NO_2Cl$ | 270 | 81·5 |
| $BF_3$ | 254 | 67·8 | $NOBr$ | 273 | 110·0 |
| $B_2H_6$ | 233 | 27·7 | $O_3$ | 239 | 48·0 |
| $B_5H_9$ | 276 | 63·1 | $P_4$ | 280 | 124·0 |
| $BiCl_3$ | 358 | 315·4 | $PH_3$ | 210 | 34·0 |
| $BrF_3$ | 292 | 136·9 | $PF_3$ | 268 | 88·0 |
| $BrF_5$ | 320 | 174·9 | $PCl_3$ | 312 | 137·4 |
| $CO_2$ | 214 | 44·0 | $PCl_5$ | 363 | 208·3 |
| $CS_2$ | 238 | 78·0 | $POCl_3$ | 325 | 153·4 |
| $COS$ | 231 | 60·1 | $PBr_3$ | 348 | 270·7 |
| $CSCl_2$ | 293 | 115·0 | $PSCl_3$ | 332 | 169·5 |
| $ClF_3$ | 285 | 92·5 | $ReF_6$ | 346 | 300·2 |
| $ClO_2$ | 251 | 67·5 | $SO_2$ | 248 | 64·1 |
| $Cl_2O$ | 266 | 86·9 | $SO_3$ | 256 | 80·1 |
| $F_2O$ | 247 | 54·0 | $SF_6$ | 290 | 146·1 |
| $GeBr_4$ | 397 | 392·5 | $SOF_2$ | 250 | 86·1 |
| $GeCl_4$ | 348 | 214·4 | $S_2Cl_2$ | 328 | 135·0 |
| $GeF_4$ | 303 | 148·6 | $SOCl_2$ | 308 | 119·0 |
| $GeH_4$ | 214 | 76·6 | $SbCl_3$ | 338 | 228·1 |
| $GeH_3Cl$ | 264 | 111·1 | $SeF_6$ | 314 | 193·0 |
| $H_2O$ | 189 | 18·0 | $SiH_4$ | 205 | 32·1 |
| $H_2O_2$ | 233 | 34·0 | $SiF_4$ | 282 | 104·1 |
| $H_2S$ | 205 | 34·1 | $SiCl_4$ | 331 | 169·9 |
| $H_2Se$ | 219 | 81·2 | $SiH_2Cl_2$ | 284 | 101·0 |
| $HN_3$ | 239 | 43·0 | $SiH_2Br_2$ | 309 | 190·1 |
| $HNO_2$ | 255 | 47·0 | $SiH_3Br$ | 263 | 111·1 |
| $HNO_3$ | 267 | 63·0 | $SnBr_4$ | 413 | 438·4 |
| $HCN$ | 202 | 27·0 | $SnCl_4$ | 365 | 260·5 |
| $IF_5$ | 329 | 221·9 | $TeF_6$ | 338 | 241·6 |
| $IF_7$ | 346 | 259·9 | $TiBr_4$ | 397 | 367·6 |
| $MoF_6$ | 331 | 210·0 | $TiCl_4$ | 352 | 189·7 |
| $N_2H_4$ | 240 | 32·0 | $TiF_4$ | 306 | 123·9 |
| $NH_3$ | 192 | 17·0 | $UF_6$ | 380 | 352·1 |
| $N_2O$ | 220 | 44·0 | $WF_6$ | 372 | 297·9 |
| $NO_2$ | 240 | 46·0 | | | |

The rigorous calculation of the total entropy of a gas is generally a formidable problem, especially in the case of polyatomic molecules for which estimations are most commonly required. The main difficulties arise in determining the rotational, vibrational and electronic components of the entropy; the translational component is easily obtained from the Sackur-Tetrode equation

$$S^\circ_{trans} = \tfrac{3}{2}R \ln M + \tfrac{5}{2} \ln T - 9 \cdot 7,$$

which with $T = 298 \cdot 2$ K simplifies to

$$S^\circ_{trans} = 109 + 28 \cdot 7 \log_{10} M \quad J\,K^{-1}\,mol^{-1}.$$

The magnitude of $S^\circ_{trans}$ is shown by the lower curve in Figure 19.

It is interesting that the contribution of $S^\circ_{trans}$ does not vary much – from 150 to 180 J K$^{-1}$ mol$^{-1}$ over a molecular weight range of 30–400. Over the same range, the other components contribute an additional 60–210 J K$^{-1}$ mol$^{-1}$ to the entropy of polyatomic molecules.

The entropy of the hypothetical molecule $HN_3Cl_4$ (whose enthalpy of formation was estimated in section 4.5.1) in the ideal gas state is thus, from equation (b) above with $M = 185$, about 340 J K$^{-1}$ mol$^{-1}$. If the entropy of vaporization is assumed to be 88 J K$^{-1}$ mol$^{-1}$ (see section 4.4), then $S^\circ_{298}$ for $HN_3Cl_4(l) = 340 - 88 = 252$ J K$^{-1}$ mol$^{-1}$.

Hence $\Delta S^\circ_f = S^\circ_{298}, HN_3Cl_4(l) - \tfrac{1}{2}S^\circ_{298}, H_2(g) - 1\tfrac{1}{2}S^\circ_{298}, N_2(g) - 2S^\circ_{298}, Cl_2(g)$

$$= 252 - 65 - 287 - 446$$

$$= -546 \text{ J K}^{-1}\,mol^{-1}.$$

Therefore the estimated free energy of formation of $HN_3Cl_4(l)$ is

$$\Delta G^\circ_f = \Delta H^\circ_f - T\,\Delta S^\circ_f$$

$$= 607 - \frac{298(-546)}{1000}$$

$$= 770 \text{ kJ mol}^{-1}.$$

The free energy of formation of $HN_3Cl_4(l)$ is thus likely to be highly positive, a circumstance to which both the endothermicity of the reaction (section 4.5.1) and the substantial entropy loss (consequent upon the decrease in the number of gaseous molecules) contribute.

# Chapter 5
# Energetics of Inorganic Substances in Solution

## 5.1 Aqueous solutions

### 5.1.1 *Standard states*

In order to make use of the standard thermodynamic quantities $\Delta G^\circ$, $\Delta H^\circ$ and $S^\circ$ it is necessary to define the standard states to which these symbols refer.

For solids, liquids and gases the standard states were defined in Chapter 1 and are summarized here for convenience:

*Solids and liquids.* The standard state at 298 K is the pure substance at one atmosphere pressure.

*Gases.* The standard state at 298 K is the ideal gas at one atmosphere pressure. The behaviour of most *real* gases corresponds closely to ideality at 298 K and one atmosphere pressure.

For *aqueous solutions*, the standard state at 298 K is a hypothetical state: it is taken as the ideal solution of unit molality at one atmosphere pressure, in which the activity of the solute is unity. The solute thus has the properties it would possess in an infinitely dilute solution, in which interactions between the solute particles are negligible. The symbol (aq) is used to denote this standard state: e.g. $Cl_2(aq)$, $NaCl(aq)$, etc.

Thus $\Delta G_f^\circ$, $\Delta H_f^\circ$ and $\Delta S_f^\circ$ for $NaCl(aq)$ refer to the process

$$Na(s) + \tfrac{1}{2}Cl_2(g) \rightarrow NaCl(aq).$$

in which the reacting elements are pure sodium metal at 298 K and one atmosphere pressure, and pure chlorine gas in the ideal gas state at 298 K and one atmosphere pressure; the product is an ideal solution of unit molality (1 mole NaCl in 1 kg of pure water) at 298 K and one atmosphere pressure.

### 5.1.2 *Individual ions*

It is possible to assign values of $\Delta G_f^\circ$, $\Delta H_f^\circ$ and $S_{298}^\circ$ to *individual aqueous ions* if the convention is adopted that each of these quantities is zero for the aqueous hydrogen ion $H^+(aq)$ in its standard state.

For example, in the case of HCl(aq), $\Delta G_f^\circ = -131\cdot2\,\text{kJ mol}^{-1}$, $\Delta H_f^\circ = -167\cdot4\,\text{kJ mol}^{-1}$ and $S_{298}^\circ = 55\cdot2\,\text{J K}^{-1}\,\text{mol}^{-1}$. Since aqueous HCl is a strong electrolyte and fully ionized in dilute solution, the symbol HCl(aq) is the equivalent of $H^+(aq) + Cl^-(aq)$. If to $H^+(aq)$ the values

$$\Delta G_f^\circ = 0 \qquad \Delta H_f^\circ = 0 \qquad S_{298}^\circ = 0$$

are assigned, then for the aqueous chloride ion $Cl^-(aq)$ in its standard state the values $\Delta G_f^\circ = -131\cdot2\,\text{kJ mol}^{-1}$, $\Delta H_f^\circ = -167\cdot4\,\text{kJ mol}^{-1}$ and $S_{298}^\circ = 55\cdot2\,\text{J K}^{-1}\,\text{mol}^{-1}$ are obtained. Thermodynamic data for some aqueous ions calculated according to this convention are collected in Table 31.

## .1.3 Preliminary discussion

As the starting point for a discussion of solution energetics, it is profitable to examine the factors which contribute to $\Delta G_f^\circ$, $\Delta H_f^\circ$ and $\Delta S_f^\circ$ for aqueous solutions of some simple inorganic compounds, and HCl(aq) and NaCl(aq) have been chosen for this purpose. It is convenient to divide the total formation reaction into two steps, the first representing the formation of the pure anhydrous substance in its standard state, and the second the dissolution of the pure substance in water to yield the hypothetical ideal solution. The data/$(\text{kJ mol}^{-1})$ for HCl(aq) and NaCl(aq) are as follows:

|  | $\Delta G_{298}^\circ$ | $\Delta H_{298}^\circ$ | $T\,\Delta S_{298}^\circ$ |
|---|---|---|---|
| (i) $\frac{1}{2}H_2(g)+\frac{1}{2}Cl_2(g) \rightarrow HCl(g)$ | $-95\cdot3$ | $-92\cdot3$ | $+2\cdot97$ |
| (ii) $\qquad HCl(g) \rightarrow HCl(aq)$ | $-35\cdot9$ | $-75\cdot1$ | $-39\cdot3$ |
| (iii) $\frac{1}{2}H_2(g)+\frac{1}{2}Cl_2(g) \rightarrow HCl(aq)$ | $-131\cdot2$ | $-167\cdot4$ | $-36\cdot33$ |
| (i) $Na(s)+\frac{1}{2}Cl_2(g) \rightarrow NaCl(s)$ | $-384\cdot0$ | $-411\cdot0$ | $-26\cdot9$ |
| (ii) $\qquad NaCl(s) \rightarrow NaCl(aq)$ | $-8\cdot99$ | $+3\cdot89$ | $+12\cdot9$ |
| (iii) $Na(s)+\frac{1}{2}Cl_2(g) \rightarrow NaCl(aq)$ | $-392\cdot99$ | $-407\cdot11$ | $-14\cdot0$ |

In each case $\Delta G^\circ$ for reaction (ii) is negative, but it is interesting that in the case of hydrogen chloride the negative sign of $\Delta G^\circ$ ($-35\cdot9$) stems from the fact that the exothermicity of the solution reaction ($\Delta H^\circ = -75\cdot1$) outweighs a moderately large decrease in entropy ($T\,\Delta S^\circ = -39\cdot3$), while in the case of sodium chloride the negative sign of $\Delta G^\circ(-8\cdot99)$ is a consequence of the fact that an entropy increase ($T\,\Delta S^\circ = +12\cdot9$) outweighs a small heat absorption ($\Delta H^\circ = +3\cdot89$). The enthalpy changes for reaction (ii) may be elucidated further by considering the process in two steps: step (iv), the formation of gaseous ions from the compound in its standard state, and step (v), the dissolution of the gaseous ion in water:

**Table 31** Thermodynamic Data for Aqueous Ions in their Standard States at 298 K

| cations | $\Delta G_f^{\circ}$ /(kJ mol$^{-1}$) | $\Delta H_f^{\circ}$ /(kJ mol$^{-1}$) | $S_{298}^{\circ}$ /(J K$^{-1}$ mol$^{-1}$) | anions | $\Delta G_f^{\circ}$ /(kJ mol$^{-1}$) | $\Delta H_f^{\circ}$ /(kJ mol$^{-1}$) | $S_{298}^{\circ}$ /(J K$^{-1}$ mol$^{-1}$) |
|---|---|---|---|---|---|---|---|
| $H^+$ | 0 | 0 | 0 | $F^-$ | −276.5 | −329.1 | −9.62 |
| $Li^+$ | −293.8 | −278.4 | 14.2 | $Cl^-$ | −131.2 | −167.4 | 55.2 |
| $Na^+$ | −261.9 | −239.7 | 60.2 | $Br^-$ | −102.8 | −120.9 | 80.7 |
| $K^+$ | −282.3 | −251.2 | 102.5 | $I^-$ | −51.7 | −55.9 | 109.4 |
| $Rb^+$ | −283.0 | −248.5 | 120.0 | $OH^-$ | −157.3 | −223.0 | −10.54 |
| $Cs^+$ | −296.2 | −261.9 | 133.1 | $SH^-$ | 12.55 | −17.15 | 6.28 |
| $Ag^+$ | 77.1 | 105.9 | 73.9 | $S^{2-}$ | 86.2 | 32.6 | −16.74 |
| $Tl^+$ | −32.4 | 5.74 | 127.2 | $ClO_2^-$ | 11.46 | −71.9 | 100.8 |
| $NH_4^+$ | −79.5 | −132.8 | 112.8 | $ClO_3^-$ | −2.51 | −98.3 | 163 |
| $Mg^{2+}$ | −456.0 | −461.9 | −118.0 | $ClO_4^-$ | −10.33 | −132.0 | 180.7 |
| $Ca^{2+}$ | −553.1 | −543.0 | −55.2 | $SO_4^{2-}$ | −741.8 | −907.5 | 17.15 |
| $Sr^{2+}$ | −557.3 | −545.5 | −39.3 | $HSO_4^-$ | −752.7 | −885.7 | 127.7 |
| $Ba^{2+}$ | −560.6 | −538.4 | 12.5 | $SeO_3^-$ | −373.8 | −512.1 | 16.32 |
| $Mn^{2+}$ | −227.6 | −223.0 | −83.7 | $SeO_4^{2-}$ | −440.9 | −607.9 | 23.9 |
| $Fe^{2+}$ | −84.9 | −87.9 | −113.4 | $HSeO_4^-$ | −452.7 | −598.7 | 92.0 |
| $Cu^{2+}$ | 65.0 | 64.4 | −98.7 | $NO_2^-$ | −34.5 | −106.3 | 125.1 |
| $Zn^{2+}$ | −147.2 | −152.4 | −106.5 | $NO_3^-$ | −110.6 | −206.6 | 146.4 |
| $Cd^{2+}$ | −77.7 | −72.4 | −61.1 | $PO_4^{3-}$ | −1025.4 | −1284 | −217.6 |
| $Hg^{2+}$ | 164.8 | 174 | −22.6 | $HPO_4^{2-}$ | −1094.1 | −1299 | −35.9 |
| $Sn^{2+}$ | −26.2 | −10.0 | −24.7 | $H_2PO_4^-$ | −1135 | −1302 | 89.1 |
| $Pb^{2+}$ | −24.4 | 1.63 | 21.3 | $HAsO_4^{2-}$ | −707.0 | −898.7 | 3.77 |

**Table 31**—*Continued*

| cations | $\Delta G_f^\circ$ /(kJ mol$^{-1}$) | $\Delta H_f^\circ$ /(kJ mol$^{-1}$) | $S_{298}^\circ$ /(J K$^{-1}$ mol$^{-1}$) |
|---|---|---|---|
| Al$^{3+}$ | −466·5 | −524·6 | −313·4 |
| Fe$^{3+}$ | −10·59 | −47·7 | −293·3 |
| Ag(NH$_3$)$_2^+$ | −17·41 | −111·8 | 241·8 |

| anions | $\Delta G_f^\circ$ /(kJ mol$^{-1}$) | $\Delta H_f^\circ$ /(kJ mol$^{-1}$) | $S_{298}^\circ$ /(J K$^{-1}$ mol$^{-1}$) |
|---|---|---|---|
| H$_2$AsO$_4^-$ | −748·5 | −904·5 | 117·2 |
| HCO$_3^-$ | −587·0 | −691·1 | 93·2 |
| CO$_3^{2-}$ | −528·0 | −676·1 | −53·1 |
| CH$_3$COO$^-$ | −372·5 | −488·6 | 87·0 |
| C$_2$O$_4^{2-}$ | −666·9 | −819·6 | 44·4 |
| CN$^-$ | 165·7 | 151·0 | 118·0 |
| CNO$^-$ | −98·7 | −140·2 | 130·1 |
| PtCl$_4^{2-}$ | −384·5 | −516·3 | 175·7 |
| PtCl$_6^{2-}$ | −515·0 | −700·4 | 220·1 |
| MnO$_4^-$ | −449·3 | −542·6 | 190·0 |
| BF$_4^-$ | −1735 | −1527 | 167·4 |

|  |  | $\Delta H^{\circ}_{298}/(\text{kJ mol}^{-1})$ |
|---|---|---|
| (iv) | $HCl(g) \rightarrow H^+(g) + Cl^-(g)$ | $+1394 \cdot 5$ |
| (v) | $H^+(g) + Cl^-(g) \rightarrow H^+(aq) + Cl^-(aq)$ | $-1469 \cdot 4$ |
| (ii) | $HCl(g) \rightarrow H^+(aq) + Cl^-(aq)$ | $-74 \cdot 9$ |
| (iv) | $NaCl(s) \rightarrow Na^+(g) + Cl^-(g)$ | $+787 \cdot 4$ |
| (v) | $Na^+(g) + Cl^-(g) \rightarrow Na^+(aq) + Cl^-(aq)$ | $-783 \cdot 6$ |
| (ii) | $NaCl(s) \rightarrow Na^+(aq) + Cl^-(aq)$ | $+3 \cdot 8$ |

It is clear that for hydrogen chloride the enthalpy change for step (v) exceeds that for step (iv), while for sodium chloride the reverse is the case; for both compounds, however, $\Delta H^{\circ}$ for step (ii) represents a relatively small difference between two large quantities, and this circumstance will be discussed further in the section on solubilities (section 5.2). In the meantime it may be noted that the enthalpy of hydration of the ions $H^+(aq)$ and $Cl^-(aq)$ exceeds that of the ions $Na^+(aq) + Cl^-(aq)$ by a very large amount,

viz   $1469 \cdot 4 - 783 \cdot 6 = 685 \cdot 8$ kJ,

and this figure must represent the amount by which the enthalpy of the process $H^+(g) \rightarrow H^+(aq)$ exceeds that of $Na^+(g) \rightarrow Na^+(aq)$. The problem of the assignment of absolute hydration enthalpies to *individual* gaseous ions will be discussed in section 5.2.3.

Turning now to the entropy contribution to $\Delta G^{\circ}$ for reaction (ii), it is interesting that the sign of $T \Delta S$ is negative for hydrogen chloride, and positive for sodium chloride.

It is in this sort of situation that particular care is necessary in interpreting entropy changes (see section 1.4.3). Superficially it might be considered that the reaction

$HCl(g) \rightarrow H^+(aq) + Cl^-(aq)$

leads to an increase in the number of particles and hence to an increase in entropy. However, it is apparent that only the first step in the solution process,

viz   $HCl(g) \rightarrow H^+(g) + Cl^-(g)$,

which is a gas-phase reaction in which the number of gaseous particles is doubled, involves an entropy increase. In the second step,

viz   $H^+(g) + Cl^-(g) \rightarrow H^+(aq) + Cl^-(aq)$,

the hydration process imposes restrictions on the translational freedom of both the ions themselves and the solvent molecules, and the net result in this case is substantial entropy loss.

**134   Energetics of Inorganic Substances in Solution**

The values of $T \Delta S$ for the contributing steps are as follows:

| | $T \Delta S/(kJ\ mol^{-1})$ |
|---|---|
| $HCl(g) \rightarrow H^+(g) + Cl^-(g)$ | $+22{\cdot}5$ |
| $H^+(g) + Cl^-(g) \rightarrow H^+(aq) + Cl^-(aq)$ | $-61{\cdot}7$ |
| $HCl(g) \rightarrow H^+(aq) + Cl^-(aq)$ | $-39{\cdot}2$ |

In the case of sodium chloride, the much greater entropy increase attending the formation of gaseous ions from a crystalline solid outweighs the entropy decrease which occurs on solution of the gaseous ions, with the result that the sign of $T \Delta S$ for the total reaction is positive:

| | $T \Delta S/(kJ\ mol^{-1})$ |
|---|---|
| $NaCl(s) \rightarrow Na^+(g) + Cl^-(g)$ | $+68{\cdot}2$ |
| $Na^+(g) + Cl^-(g) \rightarrow Na^+(aq) + Cl^-(aq)$ | $-55{\cdot}3$ |
| $NaCl(s) \rightarrow Na^+(aq) + Cl^-(aq)$ | $+12{\cdot}9$ |

(The entropies $S^{\circ}_{298}$ of the gaseous ions $H^+$ $Na^+$, and $Cl^-$ necessary to evaluate $T \Delta S$ in the above processes are those calculated by R. M. Noyes, 1963, here expressed in joules per kelvin per mole.)

## 5.2 Solubility of electrolytes

Superficially this is a bewildering field. The array of well-known facts concerning the solubility of simple inorganic compounds contains many disconcerting irregularities which do not seem to conform to any straightforward set of rules. Thus the fluoride is the most soluble of the halides of silver, while in the case of calcium the reverse is the case; the solubility of hydroxides increases along the series calcium, strontium, barium, while in the case of the sulphates the trend is in the opposite direction.

Broadly speaking it may be said that solubility in water depends on the relative magnitudes of the enthalpy and entropy changes for the two processes, (a) disruption of the crystal lattice into its gaseous ions,

e.g. $NaCl(s) \rightarrow Na^+(g) + Cl^-(g)$,

and (b) dissolution of the gaseous ions in water and their concomitant solvation,

e.g. $Na^+(g) + Cl^-(g) \rightarrow Na^+(aq) + Cl^-(aq)$,

and the following examples have been chosen to illustrate the sort of thermodynamic investigations which must be made in order to clarify a given problem:

**135    Solubility of Electrolytes**

The following are the solubilities at 298 K, in moles of solute per kilo-gramme of water (i.e. the *molalities* of the saturated aqueous solutions in equilibrium with the solid phase indicated), for the halides of sodium and silver:

| Halide | Solid phase | Solubility/{mol MX $(kg \, H_2O)^{-1}$} at 298 K |
|--------|-------------|------------------------------|
| NaF  | NaF       | 0·987 |
| NaCl | NaCl      | 6·14 |
| NaBr | $NaBr.2H_2O$ | 9·19 |
| NaI  | $NaI.2H_2O$  | 12·26 |
| AgF  | $AgF.4H_2O$  | 13·97 |
| AgCl | AgCl      | $1·346 \times 10^{-5}$ |
| AgBr | AgBr      | $7·19 \times 10^{-7}$ |
| AgI  | AgI       | $1·11 \times 10^{-8}$ |

These two series have been chosen for discussion because they show contrasting behaviour in passing along the anion sequence from fluoride $F^-$ to iodide $I^-$. In the case of the sodium salts the solubility increases, whereas for the silver compounds the reverse is true.

The standard free energy changes $\Delta G^\circ_{298}$ for the process

$$MX(s) \rightarrow MX(aq),$$

that is for the conversion of one mole of the solid salt into the hypothetical ideal solution of unit molality, and the contributing enthalpy ($\Delta H^\circ_{298}$) and entropy ($T \Delta S^\circ_{298}$) terms, are as follows:

|      | $\Delta G^\circ_{298}$ /(kJ mol$^{-1}$) | $\Delta H^\circ_{298}$ /(kJ mol$^{-1}$) | $T \Delta S^\circ_{298}$ /(kJ mol$^{-1}$) |
|------|------------|------------|------------|
| NaF  | +2·6  | +0·2  | -2·4  |
| NaCl | -9·0  | +3·9  | +12·9 |
| NaBr | -17·0 | -0·6  | +16·4 |
| NaI  | -31·1 | -7·6  | +23·5 |
| AgF  | -14·4 | -20·3 | -5·9  |
| AgCl | +55·6 | +65·4 | +9·8  |
| AgBr | +70·2 | +84·4 | +14·2 |
| AgI  | +91·7 | +112·3 | +20·6 |

For the sodium salts, the progressively increasing solubility from fluoride to iodide is reflected in the increasingly negative value of $\Delta G^\circ$. Individually, the very small enthalpy contributions and numerically larger entropy con-tributions show the same trend, in that the enthalpy change $\Delta H^\circ$ tends to become less positive (or more negative) and the entropy change ($T \Delta S^\circ$) tends to become more positive (or less negative) in passing from fluoride to iodide.

For the silver salts, however, in passing from fluoride to iodide, the salts become progressively *less* soluble as $\Delta G°$ becomes more positive. Although the entropy contributions ($T\Delta S°$) show the same trend evident in the sodium series (and increasingly favour dissolution), the over-all trend in $\Delta G°$ (and thence in solubility) is determined by the tendency for the enthalpy change $\Delta H°$ (which is numerically much larger for the silver salts than for their sodium analogues) to become more positive from fluoride to iodide.

The trends in the contributing terms $\Delta H°$ and $T\Delta S°$ for each series must now be examined more closely.

*The enthalpy contribution* $\Delta H°$. If the total solution process is divided into two steps, i.e.

(i)  $\quad\quad MX(s) \rightarrow M^+(g) + X^-(g)$
(ii) $M^+(g) + X^-(g) \rightarrow M^+(aq) + X^-(aq)$

---

(iii) $\quad\quad MX(s) \rightarrow M^+(aq) + X^-(aq)$

---

then $\Delta H°$ for step (i) is the lattice enthalpy, which can be evaluated by a Born–Haber treatment of $\Delta H_f°$ for the solid salt. For step (ii), $\Delta H°$ can then be found by difference. The results for the two series of halides are as follows:

$\Delta H_{298}°/(kJ\ mol^{-1})$:

|                      | NaF      | NaCl    | NaBr    | NaI     |
|----------------------|----------|---------|---------|---------|
| step (i)             | +919·2   | +787    | +752    | +703    |
| step (ii)            | −918·8   | −783    | −753    | −711    |
| total reaction (iii) | +0·4     | +4·0    | −1      | −8      |

|                      | AgF      | AgCl    | AgBr    | AgI     |
|----------------------|----------|---------|---------|---------|
| step (i)             | +966     | +917    | +905    | +891    |
| step (ii)            | −986     | −851    | −820    | −778    |
| total reaction (iii) | −20      | +66     | +85     | +113    |

These data reveal the fact that, in the *sodium* series, the value of the hydration enthalpy (step ii) is extremely close to that of the lattice enthalpy (step i); the two contributions very nearly balance and the net $\Delta H°$ for step (iii) represents a tiny difference between two much larger quantities. For the *silver* series, the hydration enthalpy exceeds the lattice enthalpy only in the case of silver fluoride; thereafter the hydration enthalpy is always distinctly smaller and the net $\Delta H°$ for step (iii) becomes increasingly positive.

It is noteworthy that, for a given halide ion $X^-$, the hydration enthalpy for the silver salt is always greater than that for the sodium salt by 67 kJ $mol^{-1}$; this quantity must therefore represent the amount by which the hydration enthalpy of the ion $Ag^+(g)$ exceeds that of the ion $Na^+(g)$. In the case of the lattice enthalpy, however, the amount by which the value for the silver salt exceeds that for the corresponding sodium salt *increases* from the fluoride to the iodide:

|  | MF | MCl | MBr | MI |
|---|---|---|---|---|
| $(\Delta H°_{\text{lattice}}, \text{AgX}) - (\Delta H°_{\text{lattice}}, \text{NaX})$ /(kJ mol$^{-1}$) | 47 | 130 | 153 | 188 |

The source of the differing trends in $\Delta H°$ for the total reaction (iii) seems therefore to be that the silver halide crystal lattice becomes increasingly stabilized relative to the corresponding sodium halide crystal lattice in passing from fluoride to iodide, an effect which is presumably due to an increasing contribution from van der Waals forces in the silver halide lattices.

It is clear, however, that any attempt to predict or 'explain' enthalpies of solution will require a very clear understanding of the factors which determine both lattice and hydration enthalpies, particularly since the physically significant quantity is the relatively small difference between the lattice and hydration contributions.

*The entropy contribution $T\Delta S°$.* The values of $T\Delta S°$ for the two-stage solution process are as follows. The entropy, $S°_{298}$/(J K$^{-1}$ mol$^{-1}$), of each of the gas-phase ions $Na^+(147 \cdot 9)$, $Ag^+(167 \cdot 1)$, $F^-(145 \cdot 5)$, $Cl^-(153 \cdot 3)$, $Br^-(163 \cdot 4)$ and $I^-(169 \cdot 2)$ has been calculated according to the method of R. M. Noyes (1963).

$T\Delta S°_{298}$/(kJ mol$^{-1}$):

|  | NaF | NaCl | NaBr | NaI |
|---|---|---|---|---|
| step (i) | +70 | +68 | +67 | +67 |
| step (ii) | −72 | −55 | −51 | −44 |
| total reaction (iii) | −2 | +13 | +16 | +23 |

|  | AgF | AgCl | AgBr | AgI |
|---|---|---|---|---|
| step (i) | +68 | +67 | +67 | +66 |
| step (ii) | −74 | −57 | −52 | −46 |
| total reaction (iii) | −6 | +10 | +15 | +20 |

In all cases except the two fluorides sodium fluoride and silver fluoride the entropy term $T \Delta S$ for the total reaction (iii) is positive and hence favours dissolution of the salt by tending to make $\Delta G°$ negative. In these cases the entropy increase associated with the conversion of the solid crystal into gaseous ions (step i) outweighs the entropy decrease which occurs when the gaseous ions dissolve in water (step ii). For the fluorides, however, the net entropy change (reaction iii) is negative and is a consequence of the entropy loss on dissolution of the gaseous ions exceeding the entropy gain accompanying the disruption of the crystal lattice into its component gas-phase ions; presumably this state of affairs is due to hydrogen bonding of the fluoride ion in water.

These results, taken in conjunction with the enthalpy analysis already discussed, illustrate the difficulties encountered in seeking explanations of solubilities in terms of a handful of simple rules; in general each case must be individually subjected to the above sort of analysis before any considerable progress can be made towards understanding the factors which determine solubility.

5.2.1 *Absolute values of enthalpies and entropies for individual ions*

*Enthalpies.* The sums of the enthalpies of hydration of cations and anions can be obtained from energy cycles involving experimental quantities. Thus $\Delta H°_{298}$ for the reaction

$$Na^+(g) + Cl^-(g) \rightarrow Na^+(aq) + Cl^-(aq)$$

can be derived from the reaction sequence

|  | $\Delta H°_{298}/(kJ \; mol^{-1})$ (experimental) |
|---|---|
| $Na^+(g) + e \rightarrow Na(s)$ | $-610$ |
| $Cl^-(g) \rightarrow \frac{1}{2}Cl_2(g) + e$ | $+233$ |
| $Na(s) + \frac{1}{2}Cl_2(g) \rightarrow Na^+(aq) + Cl^-(aq)$ | $-407$ |

whence   $Na^+(g) + Cl^-(g) \rightarrow Na^+(aq) + Cl^-(aq) =$   $-784$.

From data such as these, relative values of $\Delta H°_{hydration}$ for individual gaseous ions can be obtained by arbitrarily assigning a zero value for the enthalpy of hydration of some selected ion, such as

$$H^+(g) \rightarrow H^+(aq) \qquad \Delta H°_{298} = 0.$$

A selection of hydration enthalpies evaluated according to this convention is given in Table 32.

**Table 32** Relative Enthalpies of Hydration of Individual Ions, $\Delta H^{\circ}_{hyd}$ /(kJ mol$^{-1}$), at 298 K Based on H$^+$ = 0

| ion | $\Delta H^{\circ}_{hyd}$ | ion | $\Delta H^{\circ}_{hyd}$ |
|---|---|---|---|
| H$^+$ | 0 | Fe$^{2+}$ | 241 |
| Li$^+$ | 570 | Co$^{2+}$ | 185 |
| Na$^+$ | 686 | Ni$^{2+}$ | 77 |
| K$^+$ | 770 | Cu$^{2+}$ | 82 |
| Rb$^+$ | 799 | Zn$^{2+}$ | 138 |
| Cs$^+$ | 828 | Cd$^{2+}$ | 376 |
| Ag$^+$ | 618 | Hg$^{2+}$ | 358 |
| Tl$^+$ | 766 | Sn$^{2+}$ | 628 |
| Be$^{2+}$ | −312 | Pb$^{2+}$ | 700 |
| Mg$^{2+}$ | 261 | Al$^{3+}$ | −1395 |
| Ca$^{2+}$ | 605 | Fe$^{3+}$ | −1156 |
| Sr$^{2+}$ | 736 | F$^-$ | −1605 |
| Ba$^{2+}$ | 875 | Cl$^-$ | −1469 |
| Cr$^{2+}$ | 279 | Br$^-$ | −1438 |
| Mn$^{2+}$ | 342 | I$^-$ | −1397 |

When added, of course, the data of Table 32 yield the correct absolute enthalpies of hydration for a given compound,

e.g.  $\Delta H^{\circ}_{hyd}$, Na$^+$(relative to H$^+$) = 686,

$\Delta H^{\circ}_{hyd}$, Cl$^-$(relative to H$^+$) = −1469,

thus  $\Delta H^{\circ}_{hyd}$, Na$^+$ + Cl$^-$(absolute) = −783 kJ mol$^{-1}$.

The absolute values of enthalpies of hydration of individual ions are not experimentally accessible, but a good deal of evidence, which has been summarized by H. F. Halliwell and S. C. Nyburg (1963), suggests that the absolute value of $\Delta H^{\circ}_{298}$ for the hydration of the proton H$^+$ is −1091 ± 10 kJ mol$^{-1}$.

If this value (−1091 kJ mol$^{-1}$) is adopted, then the absolute values of hydration enthalpies for individual ions are those collected in Table 33.

A number of important relationships emerge from a study of the data of Table 33; in particular the dependence of hydration enthalpy on the charge and on the radius of an ion is evident.

For singly charged ions – both positive and negative – $\Delta H_{hydration}$ lies between −264 and −515 kJ mol$^{-1}$; the value for the proton H$^+$ is, as expected, exceptionally high. For bipositive ions the range is much higher, viz from −1305 to −2494 kJ mol$^{-1}$, while the two tripositive ions listed have values of about −4600 kJ mol$^{-1}$.

**Table 33** Absolute Enthalpies of Hydration of Individual Ions, $\Delta H_{hyd}^{\circ}$ /(kJ mol$^{-1}$), at 298 K Assuming H$^{+}$ = −1134 kJ mol$^{-1}$

| ion | $\Delta H_{hyd}^{\circ}$ | ion | $\Delta H_{hyd}^{\circ}$ |
|---|---|---|---|
| H$^{+}$ | −1091 | Fe$^{2+}$ | −1946 |
| Li$^{+}$ | −519 | Co$^{2+}$ | −1996 |
| Na$^{+}$ | −406 | Ni$^{2+}$ | −2105 |
| K$^{+}$ | −322 | Cu$^{2+}$ | −2100 |
| Rb$^{+}$ | −293 | Zn$^{2+}$ | −2046 |
| Cs$^{+}$ | −264 | Cd$^{2+}$ | −1807 |
| Ag$^{+}$ | −473 | Hg$^{2+}$ | −1824 |
| Tl$^{+}$ | −326 | Sn$^{2+}$ | −1552 |
| Be$^{2+}$ | −2494 | Pb$^{2+}$ | −1481 |
| Mg$^{2+}$ | −1921 | Al$^{3+}$ | −4665 |
| Ca$^{2+}$ | −1577 | Fe$^{3+}$ | −4430 |
| Sr$^{2+}$ | −1443 | F$^{-}$ | −515 |
| Ba$^{2+}$ | −1305 | Cl$^{-}$ | −381 |
| Cr$^{2+}$ | −1904 | Br$^{-}$ | −347 |
| Mn$^{2+}$ | −1841 | I$^{-}$ | −305 |

Also, within a group of the periodic table, the hydration enthalpy diminishes in magnitude as the crystal radius increases, as the examples of Table 34 demonstrate. The radii/(nm) are Pauling's (Table 20, pp. 81–2).

There is a theoretical basis for these trends. The change in free energy which accompanies the transfer of a gaseous ion into a medium of dielectric constant $D$ is given by the Born equation,

$$\Delta G^{\circ} = -\frac{N_A z^2 e^2}{8\pi\varepsilon_0 r}\left(1-\frac{1}{D}\right),$$

**Table 34** Relation of $\Delta H_{hyd}^{\circ}$ to Ionic Radius

| $\Delta H_{hyd}^{\circ}$ /(kJ mol$^{-1}$) | | $r$/nm | $\Delta H_{hyd}^{\circ}$ /(kJ mol$^{-1}$) | | $r$/nm | $\Delta H_{hyd}^{\circ}$ /(kJ mol$^{-1}$) | | $r$/nm |
|---|---|---|---|---|---|---|---|---|
| Li$^{+}$ | −519 | 0·060 | F$^{-}$ | −515 | 0·136 | Be$^{2+}$ | −2494 | 0·031 |
| Na$^{+}$ | −406 | 0·095 | Cl$^{-}$ | −381 | 0·181 | Mg$^{2+}$ | −1921 | 0·065 |
| K$^{+}$ | −322 | 0·133 | Br$^{-}$ | −347 | 0·195 | Ca$^{2+}$ | −1577 | 0·099 |
| Rb$^{+}$ | −293 | 0·148 | I$^{-}$ | −305 | 0·216 | Sr$^{2+}$ | −1443 | 0·113 |
| Cs$^{+}$ | −264 | 0·169 | | | | Ba$^{2+}$ | −1305 | 0·135 |

where $N_A$ is Avogadro's constant, $z$ is the numerical value of the charge on the ion, $e$ is the electronic charge, $r$ is the radius of the ion, and $D$ is the dielectric constant of the solvent (for water $D = 78$ at 298 K).

The corresponding entropy change, obtained from the temperature coefficient of $\Delta G°$, is

$$\Delta S° = \frac{N_A z^2 e^2}{8\pi\varepsilon_0\, Dr}\left(\frac{\partial \ln D}{\partial T}\right)_p.$$

Upon insertion of the numerical values of the known quantities, and taking $\left(\dfrac{\partial \ln D}{\partial T}\right) = -0\cdot0046$, these equations reduce to

$$\Delta G° = -68\cdot6\,\frac{z^2}{r}\ \text{kJ mol}^{-1} \tag{5.1}$$

and

$$\Delta S° = -4\cdot10\,\frac{z^2}{r}\ \text{J K}^{-1}\,\text{mol}^{-1}, \tag{5.2}$$

where $r$ is expressed in nanometres.

The expression for $\Delta H°$, obtained from 5.1, 5.2 and the relationship $\Delta H° = \Delta G° + T\,\Delta S°$ with $T = 298\cdot2$ K, is

$$\Delta H° = -69\cdot9\,\frac{z^2}{r}\ \text{kJ mol}^{-1}.$$

If Pauling's crystal radii (Table 20, pp. 81–2) are used for $r$, the values of $\Delta H°$ so calculated are in poor agreement with experiment, a result attributable principally to the inadequacy of the crystal radii as a measure of the ionic radius in solution, and secondarily to the fact that the dielectric constant $D$ of the solvent is unlikely to remain unchanged in the vicinity of a charged ion. Various attempts have been made to improve the Born equation, usually by adjusting the crystal radii to values more appropriate to the aqueous environment. Phillips and Williams (1965), for example, have shown that many enthalpies of hydration of gaseous ions roughly fit the essentially empirical equation

$$\Delta H° = -69\cdot9\left(\frac{z^2}{r+k}\right)\ \text{kJ mol}^{-1},$$

where $k$ is a constant equal to zero for anions and to $0\cdot085$ nm for cations. $r+k$ is referred to as the 'effective' radius of the ion in water. The dependence of $\Delta H°$ on the square of the ionic charge, and its inverse dependence on the ionic radius, as illustrated by the figures quoted above, are therefore clear.

*Entropies.* From the experimental $\Delta G°$ and $\Delta H°$ values for the dissolution of a salt, the entropy change $\Delta S°$ which accompanies the solution process can be calculated from the familiar equation $\Delta G° = \Delta H° - T\,\Delta S°$.

Thus for the reaction

NaCl(s) $\rightarrow$ NaCl(aq),

$$\Delta S^\circ = -\left(\frac{\Delta G^\circ - \Delta H^\circ}{T}\right) = -\left(\frac{-8995 - 3891}{298 \cdot 2}\right) = 43 \cdot 2 \text{ J K}^{-1} \text{ mol}^{-1}.$$

Hence   $S^\circ$, Na$^+$(aq) + $S^\circ$, Cl$^-$(aq) − $S^\circ$, NaCl(s) = 43·2.

Since        $S^\circ$, NaCl(s) = 72·4 J K$^{-1}$ mol$^{-1}$,

$S^\circ$, Na$^+$(aq) + $S^\circ$, Cl$^-$(aq) = 43·2 + 72·4

$$= 115 \cdot 6 \text{ J K}^{-1} \text{ mol}^{-1}.$$

Thus the experimental data yield, as was the case for enthalpies, the sum of the entropies of the constituent ions.

If the arbitrary value zero is assigned to $S^\circ_{298}$ for H$^+$(aq), relative values of individual ionic entropies are obtained; these are the values listed in Table 31.

There is a considerable amount of evidence (see, for example, R. M. Noyes, 1962) which suggests that the absolute entropy of the aqueous hydrogen ion H$^+$(aq) is in fact not far from zero; the true value probably lies between 0 and $-16$ J K$^{-1}$ mol$^{-1}$. Therefore no great error is introduced by assuming that the $S^\circ_{298}$ values of Table 31 are absolute rather than relative entropies.

**Table 35**   Entropies of Hydration at 298 K (Assuming $S^\circ_{298}$, H$^+$(aq) = 0) and Related Data

| Ion | $S^\circ_{298}$, M$^+$(g)* /(J K$^{-1}$ mol$^{-1}$) | $S^\circ_{298}$, M$^+$(aq)† /(J K$^{-1}$ mol$^{-1}$) | $\Delta S^\circ_{298}$ /(J K$^{-1}$mol$^{-1}$) | $T\Delta S^\circ_{298}$ /(kJ mol$^{-1}$) | $\Delta H^\circ_{298}$‡ /(kJ mol$^{-1}$) |
|---|---|---|---|---|---|
| H$^+$ | 109 | 0 | −109 | −33 | −1134 |
| Li$^+$ | 133 | 14 | −119 | −35 | −519 |
| Na$^+$ | 148 | 60 | −88 | −26 | −406 |
| K$^+$ | 154 | 103 | −51 | −15 | −322 |
| Rb$^+$ | 164 | 120 | −44 | −13 | −293 |
| Cs$^+$ | 170 | 133 | −37 | −11 | −264 |
| Ag$^+$ | 167 | 74 | −93 | −28 | −473 |
| F$^-$ | 146 | −10 | −156 | −47 | −515 |
| Cl$^-$ | 153 | 55 | −98 | −29 | −381 |
| Br$^-$ | 164 | 81 | −83 | −25 | −347 |
| I$^-$ | 169 | 109 | −60 | −18 | −305 |

* Calculated according to the method of R. M. Noyes (1963)
† from Table 31
‡ from Table 33

If this assumption is made, the entropy of hydration – that is $\Delta S^\circ_{298}$ for the process $M^{+or-}(g) \rightarrow M^{+or-}(aq)$ – for a number of ions can be calculated; some typical results together with related data are shown in Table 35.

The points that emerge from the data of Table 35 are:

(a) the hydration of a gaseous ion is exothermic, that is $\Delta H^\circ$ is negative.

(b) the hydration process is accompanied by a decrease in entropy ($\Delta S^\circ$ negative), apparently because the translational freedom of the ions is restricted by the solvating water molecules.

(c) the enthalpy change $\Delta H^\circ$ is numerically much larger than the entropy contribution ($T \Delta S^\circ$) to the free energy change and hence dominates $\Delta G^\circ$ for the hydration process.

(d) for groups of related ions – such as the alkali metal cations or halide anions – there is a rough direct proportionality between $\Delta H^\circ$ and $\Delta S^\circ$ (or $T \Delta S^\circ$).

### 5.2.2 *Estimation of entropies of aqueous ions*

R. E. Powell and W. M. Latimer (1951) have shown that the experimental entropies ($S^\circ_{298}$, Table 31) for monatomic aqueous ions fit the empirical equation

$$S^\circ_{298}\ (\mathrm{J\ K^{-1}\ mol^{-1}}) = \tfrac{3}{2}R \ln M + 155 - 11 \cdot 3 \frac{z}{(r+k')^2},$$

where $M$ is the atomic weight, $z$ is the numerical value of the charge on the ion, $r/\mathrm{nm}$ is the Pauling ionic radius (Table 20) and $k'/\mathrm{nm}$ is 0.20 for cations and 0·10 for anions.

This relationship may be used to estimate $S^\circ_{298}$ for monatomic aqueous ions in cases where experimental data are lacking. Transition metal ions in which more than one electronic state is significantly occupied at 298 K require the addition of an extra term to the above equation. If the energies of the occupied levels are known, the extra term can be evaluated by the methods of statistical mechanics; its upper limit is $R \ln n$, where $n$ is the multiplicity of the ground state.

In the case of complex ions, a number of empirical equations for $S^\circ_{298}$ have been developed; see, for example, J. W. Cobble (1953), and A. M. Couture and K. J. Laidler (1957).

### 5.3 Electrode potentials

#### 5.3.1 *E.M.F. of a galvanic cell*

The electromotive force of a galvanic cell under standard conditions, $\mathscr{E}^\circ$, is a measure of the free energy change $\Delta G^\circ$ for the cell reaction. The standard conditions are defined to correspond to those applicable to standard free energy changes: solids and liquids involved in the electrode reactions are the pure substances; gases are at a pressure of one atmosphere; solutions are ideal solutions of unit molality. The relation between the cell e.m.f. and the free energy change at 298 K is

$$\Delta G° = -nF\mathscr{E}°,$$

where $n$ is the number of moles of electrons transferred at each electrode, and $F$ is the Faraday, the quantity of electrical charge associated with one mole of electrons; if $\Delta G°$ is expressed in joules per mole, and $\mathscr{E}°$ in volts, then $F = 9·648 \times 10^4$ C mol$^{-1}$.

Since the sign of the free energy change $\Delta G°$ is negative for reactions which can occur spontaneously, the sign of $\mathscr{E}°$ will be positive for cell reactions which can proceed of their own accord.

For example, the cell represented by the diagram

$$\text{Zn(s)}|\text{Zn}^{2+}\text{(aq)}||\text{H}^+\text{(aq)}|\text{Pt, H}_2\text{(g, 1 atm)} \qquad \textbf{5.3}$$

consists of one electrode of zinc metal immersed in an ideal solution of $\text{Zn}^{2+}$ ions of unit molality, connected by a salt bridge (symbolized $||$) to a second electrode of hydrogen gas at one atmosphere pressure in contact with platinum metal immersed in an ideal solution of $\text{H}^+$ ions of unit molality.

The cell reaction which tends to occur spontaneously is

$$\text{Zn(s)} + 2\text{H}^+\text{(aq)} \rightarrow \text{Zn}^{2+}\text{(aq)} + \text{H}_2\text{(g)}$$

and hence the cell e.m.f. is positive; $\mathscr{E}° = +0·76$ V.

The cell diagram **5.3** is, by convention, always written in such a way that oxidation (electron loss) occurs at the left-hand electrode. If the cell diagram is written in the reverse sense as

$$\text{Pt, H}_2\text{(g, 1 atm)}|\text{H}^+\text{(aq)}||\text{Zn}^{2+}\text{(aq)}|\text{Zn(s)} \qquad \textbf{5.4}$$

then the cell reaction would be, with oxidation again occurring at the left hand electrode,

$$\text{H}_2\text{(g)} + \text{Zn}^{2+}\text{(aq)} \rightarrow 2\text{H}^+\text{(aq)} + \text{Zn(s)}.$$

Since this reaction does not tend to occur spontaneously, the sign of its e.m.f. is negative; $\mathscr{E}° = -0·76$ V.

### 5.3.2  *Standard electrode potentials*

Since the total reaction in a galvanic cell,

e.g.  $\text{Zn(s)} + 2\text{H}^+\text{(aq)} \rightarrow \text{Zn}^{2+}\text{(aq)} + \text{H}_2\text{(g)},$

can always be represented as the sum of an oxidation step and a reduction step, viz     $Zn(s) - 2e \rightarrow Zn^{2+}(aq)$   (oxidation)

and   $2H^+(aq) + 2e \rightarrow H_2(g)$   (reduction),

it is convenient to regard the cell e.m.f. (the only measurable quantity) as being the sum of two individual *electrode potentials, half-cell potentials*, or $E°$ *values*. For this purpose it is, of course, necessary to assign an arbitrary electrode potential to a suitably chosen reference electrode; the hydrogen electrode has been selected as the reference standard and is by convention assigned $E° = 0.00$ V.

These standard half-cell potentials or $E°$ values are known as *standard electrode potentials* or standard reduction potentials, since the half-cell reaction to which $E°$ refers is by convention written as a reduction, e.g. for the half-cell reaction

$Zn^{2+}(aq) + 2e \rightarrow Zn(s)$,

$E°(Zn^{2+}|Zn) = -0.76$ V.

This, of course, corresponds to the $\mathscr{E}°$ value for the complete cell **5.4** above.

5.3.3   *Factors contributing to the magnitude of a standard electrode potential $E°$*

It is of interest to inquire into the factors which determine the sign and magnitude of $E°$, and for this purpose a series of unipositive metal ions which on reduction yield the pure metal has been chosen:

| half-cell reaction | $E°/V$ |
|---|---|
| $Li^+ + e \rightarrow Li$ | $-3.04$ |
| $Na^+ + e \rightarrow Na$ | $-2.71$ |
| $K^+ + e \rightarrow K$ | $-2.92$ |
| $Rb^+ + e \rightarrow Rb$ | $-2.91$ |
| $Cs^+ + e \rightarrow Cs$ | $-2.92$ |
| $Ag^+ + e \rightarrow Ag$ | $+0.80$ |

The noteworthy features of this group of metals are (a) the irregularity of the alkali metal series, which is unusual in so 'well-behaved' a periodic group, and (b) the marked contrast between the high, negative values of the alkali metals and the moderately positive value for silver.

The standard electrode potential $E°$ for the half-cell $M^+(aq)|M(s)$ is equal to $-nF\Delta G°$, where $\Delta G°$ is the standard free energy change for the complete cell reaction

$\frac{1}{2}H_2(g) + M^+(aq) \rightarrow H^+(aq) + M(s)$.

The steps which may be envisaged as contributing to the total reaction are as follows:

| (i)   | $M^+(aq) \rightarrow M^+(g)$ |
| (ii)  | $M^+(g) + e \rightarrow M(g)$ |
| (iii) | $M(g) \rightarrow M(s)$ |
| (iv)  | $\frac{1}{2}H_2(g) \rightarrow H(g)$ |
| (v)   | $H(g) \rightarrow H^+(g) + e$ |
| (vi)  | $H^+(g) \rightarrow H^+(aq)$ |

---

$$M^+(aq) + \tfrac{1}{2}H_2(g) \rightarrow M(s) + H^+(aq),$$

---

and the values of $\Delta H^\circ$, $T \Delta S^\circ$ and $\Delta G^\circ$ for each step at 298 K are shown in Table 36.

Since $E^\circ$ depends on so many factors, it is not possible to explain the differences in its sign and magnitude observable in the above group of metals in terms of any one of them. However, the positive $E^\circ$ for the $Ag^+|Ag$ electrode is largely attributable to the high enthalpy of sublimation of silver metal (step iii) and to the high ionization enthalpy of the gaseous atom (step ii). In the alkali metal series, a comparison of lithium and sodium is instructive. Because of the small radius of its ion – $r$(Pauling) $Li^+ = 0.060$ nm, cf. $Na^+ = 0.095$ nm – and the high ionization enthalpy of the neutral atom, it might be expected that $Li^+$ ion would more readily accept electrons and undergo reduction to the metal than would be the case for $Na^+$ ion. Indeed the process

$$Li^+(g) + e \rightarrow Li(s),$$

with $\Delta H^\circ_{298} = -687$ kJ mol$^{-1}$, proceeds more exothermically than the process

$$Na^+(g) + e \rightarrow Na(s),$$

for which $\Delta H^\circ_{298} = -610$ kJ mol$^{-1}$; that is the *gaseous* ions $Li^+$ is more easily reduced than the *gaseous* $Na^+$ ion.

However, the enthalpy of hydration of $Li^+(g)$ is much higher than that of $Na^+(g)$, with the consequence that the reaction involving the reduction of *aqueous* ions,

$$M^+(aq) + \tfrac{1}{2}H_2(g) \rightarrow M(s) + H^+(aq),$$

occurs more endothermically for $Li^+(aq)$ than for $Na^+(aq)$. Since the $T \Delta S^\circ$ terms differ by only 7 kJ mol$^{-1}$, $\Delta G^\circ$ for this reaction is more positive for lithium than for sodium, that is the $Li^+|Li$ half-cell has the more negative $E^\circ$ value.

Another case of interest concerns the metals zinc and copper; the former (zinc) has $E^\circ = -0.76$ V, while the latter (copper) has $E^\circ = +0.34$ V. Clearly $Cu^{2+}(aq)$ ions are more readily reduced than $Zn^{2+}(aq)$ ions by a very

**Table 36**  Thermodynamic Data for Steps Contributing to Standard Electrode Potentials

|  | Li | Na | K | Rb | Cs | Ag |
|---|---|---|---|---|---|---|
| $\Delta H^\circ_{298}/(\text{kJ mol}^{-1})$: | | | | | | |
| *step* | | | | | | |
| (i) | −570 | −686 | −770 | −797 | −828 | −618 |
| (ii) | −526 | −502 | −425 | −409 | −382 | −737 |
| (iii) | −161 | −108 | −90 | −82 | −78 | −286 |
| (iv) | 218 | 218 | 218 | 218 | 218 | 218 |
| (v) | 1318 | 1318 | 1318 | 1318 | 1318 | 1318 |
| (vi) | 0 | 0 | 0 | 0 | 0 | 0 |
| | 279 | 240 | 251 | 248 | 248 | −105 |
| $T\Delta S^\circ_{298}/(\text{kJ mol}^{-1})$: | | | | | | |
| | −15 | −22 | −31 | −35 | −34 | −29 |
| $\Delta G^\circ_{298}/(\text{kJ mol}^{-1})$: | | | | | | |
| | 294 | 262 | 282 | 283 | 282 | 76 |
| $E^\circ/\text{V}$ | −3·04 | −2·71 | −2·92 | −2·92 | −2·92 | +0·80 |

Sources of data:

$\Delta H^\circ_{298}$: steps (i) and (vi), Table 32; steps (ii) and (v), Table 12, adjusted to values of $\Delta H^\circ_{298}$ in kJ mol$^{-1}$; steps (iii) and (iv), Table 10

$T\Delta S^\circ_{298}$: These values, with $T = 298·2$ K, were derived from the experimental entropies:
$S^\circ$, M(s) + $S^\circ$, H$^+$(aq) − $\frac{1}{2} S^\circ$, H$_2$(g) − $S^\circ$, M$^+$(aq). $S^\circ$ values for M$^+$(aq) and H$^+$(aq) are from Table 31. $S^\circ$ for H$_2$(g) = 131 J K$^{-1}$ mol$^{-1}$. For M(s) the values of $S^\circ$ (J K$^{-1}$ mol$^{-1}$) are Li = 28, Na = 51, K = 64, Rb = 69, Cs = 83, Ag = 43.

substantial margin, which is a surprising (albeit familiar) fact in view of the proximity of the two metals in the first transition series. A thermodynamic analysis of their $E^\circ$ values is as follows:

| $\Delta H^\circ_{298}/(\text{kJ mol}^{-1})$: | | Zn | Cu |
|---|---|---|---|
| (i) | $M^{2+}(aq) \rightarrow M^{2+}(g)$ | $-138$ | $-82$ |
| (ii) | $M^{2+}(g) + 2e \rightarrow M(g)$ | $-2651$ | $-2715$ |
| (iii) | $M(g) \rightarrow M(s)$ | $-131$ | $-339$ |
| (iv) | $H_2(g) \rightarrow 2H(g)$ | $436$ | $436$ |
| (v) | $2H(g) \rightarrow 2H^+(g) + 2e$ | $2635$ | $2635$ |
| (vi) | $2H^+(g) \rightarrow 2H^+(aq)$ | $0$ | $0$ |
| (vii) | $M^{2+}(aq) + H_2(g) \rightarrow M(s) + 2H^+(aq)$ | $151$ | $-65$ |
| $T\Delta S^\circ_{298}/(\text{kJ mol}^{-1})$: | | $5$ | $0\cdot4$ |
| $\Delta G^\circ_{298}/(\text{kJ mol}^{-1})$: | | $146$ | $-65$ |
| $E^\circ/\text{V}$: | | $-0\cdot76$ | $+0\cdot34$ |

The substantial difference between $E^\circ$ ($Zn^{2+}|Zn$) and $E^\circ(Cu^{2+}|Cu)$ can be traced to a similar difference in $\Delta H^\circ$ for the total reaction (vii). The smaller ionization enthalpy of Zn (step ii) is almost balanced by the higher enthalpy of hydration (step i), and most of the difference in $\Delta H^\circ$ for the total reaction is due to the much higher enthalpy of sublimation of copper metal (step iii).

### 5.3.4 *Limitations on the usefulness of $E^\circ$ values*

$E^\circ$ values, like the $\Delta G^\circ$ values to which they are related, refer to strictly defined conditions. If $E^\circ$ values are to be used to predict the feasibility of a proposed reaction, the restrictions imposed by the defined conditions must always be kept in mind. This matter was discussed fully for free energy values in section 1.4.2, and only one further example will be quoted here.

Consider the oxidation–reduction reaction in which manganese dioxide $MnO_2$ reacts with hydrochloric acid:

$$MnO_2(s) + 2Cl^-(aq) + 4H^+(aq) \rightarrow Mn^{2+}(aq) + Cl_2(g) + 2H_2O(l). \qquad \textbf{5.5}$$

This reaction can be represented as the sum of an oxidation step and a reduction step,

viz $\qquad 2Cl^-(aq) - 2e \rightarrow Cl_2(g)$

and $\quad MnO_2(s) + 4H^+(aq) + 2e \rightarrow Mn^{2+}(aq) + 2H_2O(l)$.

The appropriate standard electrode potentials are

$$Cl_2 + 2e \rightarrow 2Cl^- \qquad\qquad E^\circ_1 = +1\cdot36 \text{ V}$$

$$MnO_2 + 4H^+ + 2e \rightarrow Mn^{2+} + 2H_2O \qquad E^\circ_2 = +1\cdot23 \text{ V}$$

**Table 37** Electrode Potentials, $E°/$ V, at 298 K in Water and Liquid Ammonia

| half-cell reaction | $E°$, $H_2O$ | $E°$, $NH_3$ |
|---|---|---|
| $Li^+ + \quad e \rightarrow Li$ | $-3\cdot04$ | $-2\cdot34$ |
| $K^+ + \quad e \rightarrow K$ | $-2\cdot92$ | $-2\cdot04$ |
| $Ba^{2+} + 2e \rightarrow Ba$ | $-2\cdot90$ | $-2\cdot2$ |
| $Ca^{2+} + 2e \rightarrow Ca$ | $-2\cdot87$ | $-2\cdot17$ |
| $Na^+ + \quad e \rightarrow Na$ | $-2\cdot71$ | $-1\cdot89$ |
| $Zn^{2+} + 2e \rightarrow Zn$ | $-0\cdot76$ | $-0\cdot54$ |
| $Pb^{2+} + 2e \rightarrow Pb$ | $-0\cdot13$ | $+0\cdot28$ |
| $H^+ + \quad e \rightarrow \frac{1}{2}H_2$ | $0\cdot00$ | $0\cdot00$ |
| $Cu^{2+} + 2e \rightarrow Cu$ | $+0\cdot34$ | $+0\cdot40$ |
| $Cu^+ + \quad e \rightarrow Cu$ | $+0\cdot52$ | $+0\cdot36$ |
| $\frac{1}{2}Br_2 + \quad e \rightarrow Br^-$ | $+1\cdot07$ | $+1\cdot73$ |
| $\frac{1}{2}Cl_2 + \quad e \rightarrow Cl^-$ | $+1\cdot36$ | $+1\cdot91$ |
| $\frac{1}{2}F_2 + \quad e \rightarrow F^-$ | $+2\cdot80$ | $+3\cdot50$ |

and the cell e.m.f. for the total reaction **5.5** is obtained by subtracting $E_1°$ from $E_2°$,

i.e. $\quad \mathscr{E}° = E_2° - E_1° = 1\cdot23 - 1\cdot36$

$$= -0\cdot13 \text{ V}.$$

This negative value of $\mathscr{E}°$ corresponds to a positive value of $\Delta G_{298}°$ ($+25$ kJ mol$^{-1}$) for reaction **5.5**, which will therefore *not* occur spontaneously under the standard conditions to which the thermodynamic symbols refer. Reaction **5.5**, however, is well known as a means of generating chlorine gas in the laboratory! But the usual procedure for obtaining chlorine in this way is to *boil* $MnO_2$ with *concentrated* hydrochloric acid, and both the reaction temperature (say 373 K) and the concentrations of the reacting ions are so different from the standard conditions (temperature 298 K; unit molality) that $E°$ values have no relevance.

### 5.3.5 *Electrode potentials in non-aqueous solvents*

It is evident from the analysis given in section 5.3.3 that an $E°$ value for a metal ion–metal electrode depends, *inter alia*, on the solvation energy of the gaseous metal ion. It is therefore not surprising that electrode potentials measured in solvents other than water have different values, resulting from differences in the solvation energies. A comparison of $E°$ values for two solvents – water and liquid ammonia – is given in Table 37. These differences often signify that oxidation–reduction reactions may proceed quite differently in the two solvents.

For example, consider the reduction of copper(II) ions $Cu^{2+}$ by metallic copper to copper(I) ions,

$$Cu^{2+} + Cu \rightarrow 2Cu^+.$$

The e.m.f. $\mathscr{E}^\circ$ of a cell for which this is the cell reaction is

$$\mathscr{E}^\circ = E^\circ_{Cu^{2+}|Cu} - E^\circ_{Cu^+ \, Cu}.$$

In water solution (using the values of Table 37),

$$\mathscr{E}^\circ = 0{\cdot}34 - 0{\cdot}52 = -0{\cdot}18 \text{ V}$$

and the corresponding free energy change $\Delta G^\circ_{298}$ is given by

$$\Delta G^\circ_{298} = -nF\mathscr{E}^\circ,$$

which with $n = 2$, $F = 96\,487$ C mol$^{-1}$ and $\mathscr{E}^\circ = -0{\cdot}18$ V gives

$$\Delta G^\circ_{298} = 34{\cdot}7 \text{ kJ (mol } Cu^{2+})^{-1}.$$

The positive sign of $\Delta G^\circ$ indicates that the cell reaction would *not* proceed spontaneously. The equilibrium constant $K$ for the process

$$Cu^{2+}(aq) + Cu(s) \rightarrow 2Cu^+(aq),$$

derived from the expression

$$\Delta G_{298} = -RT \ln K$$

is $K = 8 \times 10^{-7}$,

which indicates that the hydrated copper(II) ion is reduced to only a minute extent by copper metal in aqueous solution.

In liquid ammonia solution, however,

$$\mathscr{E}^\circ = 0{\cdot}40 - 0{\cdot}36 = +0{\cdot}04 \text{ V},$$

and $\Delta G_{298} = -7{\cdot}53$ kJ (mol $Cu^{2+})^{-1}$.

The negative sign of $\Delta G^\circ$ is in contrast to the positive sign for the reaction in water solution, and the equilibrium constant

$$K = 22$$

indicates that the reduction of $Cu^{2+}$ ion by metallic copper will proceed to a marked degree in liquid ammonia.

## 5.4 The strength of inorganic acids in aqueous solution

Thermodynamic data are invaluable when seeking the causes of the differing degrees of dissociation of inorganic acids in solution. A much-discussed series is the group of halogen hydracids HX (X = F, Cl, Br, I). By invoking

**151  The Strength of Inorganic Acids in Aqueous Solutions**

the superficial and spurious argument that fluorine, by virtue of its superior electronegativity, attracts electrons from the H—X bond and thus facilitates ionization in the sense

$$H-F(aq) \rightarrow H^+(aq) + F^-(aq),$$

it might be wrongly concluded that hydrofluoric acid is the strongest of the halogen hydracids in aqueous solution. It is, of course, well known that HF is the weakest of these acids. The dissociation constant $K_a$ of the acid at 298 K is related to the free energy change $\Delta G^{\circ}_{298}$ for the process

$$HX(aq) \rightarrow H^+(aq) + X^-(aq)$$

by the relationship

$$\Delta G^{\circ}_{298} = -RT \ln K_a,$$

and $\Delta G^{\circ}_{298}$ in turn is the resultant of an enthalpy ($\Delta H^{\circ}_{298}$) and an entropy ($T \Delta S^{\circ}_{298}$) contribution:

$$\Delta G^{\circ}_{298} = \Delta H^{\circ}_{298} - T \Delta S^{\circ}_{298}.$$

It is instructive to examine the factors which influence the magnitude of the enthalpy and entropy changes, and hence the free energy change, for the dissociation of all the halogen hydracids in aqueous solution:
(a) $\Delta H^{\circ}_{298}$ *for* $HX(aq) \rightarrow H^+(aq) + X^-(aq)$. The data for the contributing series of reactions are as follows:

$\Delta H^{\circ}_{298}/(kJ\ mol^{-1})$

|  | ref. | F | Cl | Br | I |
|---|---|---|---|---|---|
| (i) $HX(aq) \rightarrow HX(g)$ | a | 48 | 18 | 21 | 23 |
| (ii) $HX(g) \rightarrow H(g) + X(g)$ | b | 566 | 431 | 366 | 299 |
| (iii) $H(g) \rightarrow H^+(g) + e$ | c | 1318 | 1318 | 1318 | 1318 |
| (iv) $X(g) + e \rightarrow X^-(g)$ | c | −339 | −354 | −330 | −301 |
| (v) $H^+(g) \rightarrow H^+(aq)$ | d | −1091 | −1091 | −1091 | −1091 |
| (vi) $X^-(g) \rightarrow X^-(aq)$ | d | −515 | −381 | −347 | −305 |
| (vii) $HX(aq) \rightarrow H^+(aq) + X^-(aq)$ |  | −13 | −59 | −63 | −57 |

a: J. C. McCoubrey (1955).
b: section 4.3.
c: Chapter 2.
d: section 5.2.1. The sum of the values for $H^+$ and $X^-$ is independent of the value assigned for the hydration of the proton.

These data reveal that $\Delta H^{\circ}_{298}$ for the total dissociation reaction (vii) does not differ much for HCl, HBr, and HI, but that for HF its value (−13 kJ mol$^{-1}$), although negative, is distinctly smaller (by 40–50 kJ mol$^{-1}$) than for the others – that is the dissociation of hydrogen fluoride in aqueous solution is only slightly exothermic. This circumstance stems from the fact that steps (i and ii) – the removal of undissociated HX molecules into the gas phase from aqueous solution, and the homolytic fission of the covalent H—X bond in the gas molecule – are both distinctly more endothermic for HF than for the other three HX molecules. Thus the high enthalpy of solution of un-ionized HX molecules (attributable in part to hydrogen bonding) and the high covalent bond energy of the HF molecule are sufficient to outweigh the effect of the high enthalpy of solution of the gaseous fluoride ion (step vi), with the result that the negative value of $\Delta H_{298}^{\circ}$ for the total reaction (vii) is quite small. The 'anomalously' low value of the electron affinity of fluorine (step iv) also contributes. It is thus clear that the small enthalpy change accompanying the ionization of HF in aqueous solution cannot be attributed to any single factor; rather it is the result of the complex interplay of several factors.

(b) $\Delta S_{298}^{\circ}$ for HX(aq) $\rightarrow$ H$^+$(aq) + X$^-$(aq). $\Delta S_{298}^{\circ}$ has been evaluated by using the experimental $S_{298}^{\circ}$ (listed in Table 31) for the aqueous ions, and assessing $S_{298}^{\circ}$ for the aqueous neutral molecules by the use of the empirical expression for such species given by R. E. Powell and W. M. Latimer (1951), viz

$$S_{298}^{\circ} = \tfrac{3}{2}R \ln M + s^{\text{int}} + 42 - 0.92\, V_{\text{m}},$$

where $M$ is the molecular weight of the neutral molecule, $s^{\text{int}}$ its internal (rotational, vibrational, and electronic) entropy, calculated on the assumption that it is the same as for the gaseous molecule, and $V_{\text{m}}$ is the molal volume of the pure anhydrous liquid.

The results are:

| | $S_{298}^{\circ}$, HX(aq) /(J K$^{-1}$ mol$^{-1}$) | $S_{298}^{\circ}$, H$^+$(aq) +X$^-$(aq) /(J K$^{-1}$ mol$^{-1}$) | $\Delta S_{298}^{\circ}$ /(J K$^{-1}$ mol$^{-1}$) | $T\Delta S_{298}^{\circ}$ /(kJ mol$^{-1}$) |
|---|---|---|---|---|
| HF | 88 | −8 | −96 | −29 |
| HCl | 92 | 54 | −38 | −13 |
| HBr | 96 | 79 | −17 | −4 |
| HI | 96 | 109 | 13 | 4 |

These data show that the entropy change accompanying ionization is least favourable for HF, and becomes less negative (and hence less unfavourable) in passing down the series to HI.

(c) $\Delta G_{298}^{\circ}$ for HX(aq) $\rightarrow$ H$^+$(aq) + X$^-$(aq). The calculated values of $\Delta G_{298}^{\circ}$ and $K_a$ are as follows:

| | $\Delta G_{298}^{\circ}$ /(kJ mol$^{-1}$) (calc.) | $K_a$ (calc.) |
|---|---|---|
| HF | +16 | $10^{-3}$ |
| HCl | −48 | $10^{8}$ |
| HBr | −58 | $10^{10}$ |
| HI | −61 | $10^{11}$ |

The calculated value of $K_a$ for HF ($10^{-3}$) compares reasonably well with the experimental value of $6 \cdot 7 \times 10^{-4}$. The large values of $K_a$ for HCl, HBr and HI are in accord with the fact that these acids are essentially fully ionized in aqueous solution.

### 5.4.1 *Successive ionization constants for acids*

It is well known that the successive ionization steps of a polyprotic acid occur with decreasing readiness, as the following typical examples demonstrate:

$H_2SO_3$: $K_1 = 1 \cdot 7 \times 10^{-2}$
$K_2 = 6 \cdot 24 \times 10^{-8}$,

$H_2S$: $K_1 = 5 \cdot 7 \times 10^{-8}$
$K_2 = 1 \cdot 2 \times 10^{-15}$,

$H_3PO_4$: $K_1 = 7 \cdot 9 \times 10^{-3}$
$K_2 = 6 \cdot 2 \times 10^{-8}$
$K_3 = 10^{-12}$.

A common explanation of this consistent trend is that whereas $K_1$ refers to the removal of a proton from a neutral molecule, $K_2$ refers to the removal of a proton from a negatively charged ion; in the latter case the ionization occurs less readily because of the electrostatic attraction between the ion and the departing proton, as in the second ionization of phosphoric acid:

In the case of $K_3$, the proton is removed from an ion carrying a net double negative charge, and occurs still less readily.

Implicit in this sort of description of the ionization process is the suggestion that the O—H bond becomes progressively more difficult to break, and that the O—H bond energy is the factor which determines the magnitude of the dissociation constant. The data of Table 38, however, establish that although

**Table 38** Thermodynamic Data for the Ionization of Phosphoric Acid (from K. S. Pitzer, 1937)

| | $\Delta G_{298}^{\circ}$ /(kJ mol$^{-1}$) | $\Delta H_{298}^{\circ}$ /(kJ mol$^{-1}$) | $\Delta S_{298}^{\circ}$ /(J K$^{-1}$ mol$^{-1}$) | $T\Delta S_{298}^{\circ}$ /(kJ mol$^{-1}$) | $K$ |
|---|---|---|---|---|---|
| $H_3PO_4 \rightarrow H^+ + H_2PO_4^-$ | $+12 \cdot 1$ | $-7 \cdot 9$ | $-66 \cdot 9$ | $-20 \cdot 0$ | $K_1 = 7 \cdot 9 \times 10^{-3}$ |
| $H_2PO_4^- \rightarrow H^+ + HPO_4^{2-}$ | $+41 \cdot 0$ | $+3 \cdot 4$ | $-126 \cdot 8$ | $-37 \cdot 7$ | $K_2 = 6 \cdot 2 \times 10^{-8}$ |
| $HPO_4^{2-} \rightarrow H^+ + PO_4^{3-}$ | $+68 \cdot 2$ | $+14 \cdot 6$ | $-179 \cdot 9$ | $-53 \cdot 6$ | $K_3 = 10^{-12}$ |

$\Delta H^\circ$ for the successive steps certainly becomes less favourable for ionization, the entropy change $\Delta S^\circ$ also follows the same trend. The entropy loss $\Delta S^\circ$ for the first ionization of an inorganic acid is commonly roughly 85 $J\,K^{-1}\,mol^{-1}$, for the second about $-125\,J\,K^{-1}\,mol^{-1}$ and for the third still more negative. The fall in entropy can be attributed, at least in part, to the fact that water molecules become frozen or locked in position around the charged ions produced by the dissociation.

Furthermore, $\Delta H^\circ$ for each step is not simply a measure of the heat absorption or evolution occurring when the O—H bond is broken. The first ionization, for example, may be envisaged as proceeding in the following steps:

(i) $\qquad H_3PO_4(aq) \rightarrow H_3PO_4(g)$
(ii) $\qquad H_3PO_4(g) \rightarrow H(g) + H_2PO_4(g)$
(iii) $\qquad H(g) \rightarrow H^+(g) + e$
(iv) $\qquad H_2PO_4(g) + e \rightarrow H_2PO_4^-(g)$
(v) $\;H^+(g) + H_2PO_4^-(g) \rightarrow H^+(aq) + H_2PO_4^-(aq)$

Thus $\Delta H^\circ$ for the total reaction is determined by the O—H bond-dissociation energy (step ii), the difference between the heats of hydration of the molecule (step i) and the ions (step v), and the difference between the ionization potential of H(g) (step iii) and the electron affinity of the radical $H_2PO_4$ (step iv).

Unfortunately, the enthalpy changes for the individual steps are not all known, but the complexity of the situation is sufficiently clear to deter one from offering too glib an 'explanation' of the magnitude of a dissociation constant.

### 5.4.2 The strength of oxyacids

A number of elements give rise to series of oxyacids which differ only in the number of oxygen atoms present in the molecule – for example $HNO_2$, $HNO_3$; $H_2SO_3$, $H_2SO_4$; $HClO$, $HClO_2$, $HClO_3$, $HClO_4$ – and it is well known that within each series the acid strength increases as the proportion of oxygen rises.

Thus for HClO, $\quad K_a = 4 \cdot 0 \times 10^{-8}$,
for $HClO_2$, $\qquad K_a = 1 \cdot 1 \times 10^{-2}$,

while $HClO_3$ and $HClO_4$ are strong acids which are fully ionized in dilute solution.

Thermodynamic data for HClO and $HClO_2$ are as follows:

| | $\Delta H^\circ_{298}$ /(kJ mol$^{-1}$) | $\Delta S^\circ_{298}$ /(J K$^{-1}$ mol$^{-1}$) | $T\Delta S^\circ_{298}$ /(kJ mol$^{-1}$) | $\Delta G^\circ_{298}$ /(kJ mol$^{-1}$) | $K_a$ |
|---|---|---|---|---|---|
| $HClO \rightarrow H^+ + ClO^-$ | $+13 \cdot 9$ | $-95 \cdot 4$ | $-28 \cdot 4$ | $+42 \cdot 3$ | $4 \cdot 0 \times 10^{-8}$ |
| $HClO_2 \rightarrow H^+ + ClO^-$ | $-14 \cdot 6$ | $-86 \cdot 6$ | $-25 \cdot 8$ | $+11 \cdot 2$ | $1 \cdot 1 \times 10^{-2}$ |

It is interesting that in this case there is no great difference in the entropy terms and that the difference in $K_a$ is largely a result of the fact that while $\Delta H^\circ$ for HClO is positive ($+13\cdot9$ kJ mol$^{-1}$), the ionization of HClO$_2$ is an exothermic process with $\Delta H^\circ = -14\cdot6$ kJ mol$^{-1}$.

L. Pauling (1960, p. 326) has attributed the larger $K_a$ for HClO$_2$ to its greater reluctance to form the covalent H—OClO bond from the ions H$^+$ and ClO$_2^-$, but again it should be remembered that all the steps

$$\text{HClO}_n(\text{aq}) \rightarrow \text{HClO}_n(\text{g})$$
$$\text{HClO}_n(\text{g}) \rightarrow \text{H}(\text{g}) + \text{ClO}_n(\text{g})$$
$$\text{H}(\text{g}) + \text{ClO}_n(\text{g}) \rightarrow \text{H}^+(\text{g}) + \text{ClO}_n^-(\text{g})$$
$$\text{H}^+(\text{g}) + \text{ClO}_n^-(\text{g}) \rightarrow \text{H}^+(\text{aq}) + \text{ClO}_n^-(\text{aq})$$

contribute to the total enthalpy change. Part, at least, of the difference between HClO and HClO$_2$ may be attributable to differences in hydration enthalpy terms.

## 5.5 Complex ion formation in aqueous solution

The formation in aqueous solution of a complex ion such as hexammine nickel(II), Ni(NH$_3$)$_6^{2+}$, as represented by the equation

$$\text{Ni}^{2+}(\text{aq}) + 6\text{NH}_3(\text{aq}) \rightleftharpoons \text{Ni(NH}_3)_6^{2+}(\text{aq})$$

is actually a stepwise process in which the water molecules which hydrate the Ni$^{2+}$ ion are successively replaced by ammonia molecules. In general a hydrated metal ion M may react with a ligand L (which may be a neutral molecule like NH$_3$ or a charged ion like Cl$^-$) to give rise to a series of equilibria

$$\text{M} + \text{L} \rightleftharpoons \text{ML} \qquad k_1,$$
$$\text{ML} + \text{L} \rightleftharpoons \text{ML}_2 \qquad k_2,$$
$$\vdots$$
$$\text{ML}_{n-1} + \text{L} \rightleftharpoons \text{ML}_n \qquad k_n,$$

each with its associated equilibrium constant $k$.

A total equilibrium constant $K$ relates to the equilibrium

$$\text{M} + n\text{L} \rightleftharpoons \text{ML}_n$$

and is equal to the product of the stepwise constants,

$$K = k_1 k_2 \ldots k_n.$$

The standard free energy change $\Delta G°$ for the total reaction is related to the equilibrium constant $K$ by the equation

$$\Delta G° = -RT \ln K,$$

and is, as usual, the resultant of an enthalpy term $\Delta H°$ and an entropy term $T \Delta S°$.

The factors which influence the magnitude of $\Delta G°$ in these cases are complicated and can be discerned in a qualitative way from the following reaction sequence involving the formation of a hexa-coordinated nickel complex in aqueous solution:

Assume that the ligand L is a neutral molecule containing a donor nitrogen atom, like $NH_3$ or its substituted derivatives.

Then the total reaction is

$$Ni^{2+}(aq) + 6L(aq) \rightleftharpoons NiL_6^{2+}(aq).$$

It is usual to assume that the principal nickel species represented by the symbol $Ni^{2+}(aq)$ is the hexaquo ion $Ni(H_2O)_6^{2+}(aq)$, and that the complex-forming reaction involves the replacement of the coordinated water molecules by the ligand molecules L. The reaction may thus be represented

$$Ni(H_2O)_6^{2+}(aq) + 6L(aq) \rightleftharpoons NiL_6^{2+}(aq) + 6H_2O(l).$$

For discussion purposes it may be regarded as proceeding in the following steps:

| | |
|---|---|
| (i) | $Ni(H_2O)_6^{2+}(aq) \rightarrow Ni(H_2O)_6^{2+}(g)$ |
| (ii) | $Ni(H_2O)_6^{2+}(g) \rightarrow Ni^{2+}(g) + 6H_2O(g)$ |
| (iii) | $6H_2O(g) \rightarrow 6H_2O(l)$ |
| (iv) | $6L(aq) \rightarrow 6L(g)$ |
| (v) | $Ni^{2+}(g) + 6L(g) \rightarrow NiL_6^{2+}(g)$ |
| (vi) | $NiL_6^{2+}(g) \rightarrow NiL_6^{2+}(aq)$ |

(vii) $Ni(H_2O)_6^{2+}(aq) + 6L(aq) \rightarrow NiL_6^{2+}(aq) + 6H_2O(l)$

Each step will involve an enthalpy change $\Delta H$ and an entropy change $\Delta S$, and it is clear that $\Delta G°$ for the total reaction (vii) will be determined by the resultants of the enthalpy and entropy changes for reactions (i–vi). The multiplicity of factors contributing to $\Delta G°$ (and hence to $K$) is clearly evident.

The *total enthalpy change* ($\Delta H°$ for reaction vii) will reflect

(a) the difference between the heat of solution of the gaseous aquo ion (step i) and that of the gaseous complex ion (step vi),

(b) the difference between the heat of evaporation of water (step iii) and the heat of solution of the pure ligand (step iv), and

(c) the difference between the enthalpies of the gas-phase coordination reactions (steps ii and v).

The difference (c) is itself a complex quantity; its magnitude is determined essentially by the difference in the M—O and M—N bond strengths, but these bond energies are themselves affected by crystal field stabilization effects and the operation of repulsive forces between the ligands.

The *total entropy change* ($\Delta S°$ for reaction vii) will reflect a similar complexity of influences.

Unfortunately only steps (iii, iv and vii) can be directly measured experimentally, and a complete thermodynamic analysis based on the above reaction sequence is not possible. The following examples have been chosen to illustrate some of the effects referred to above.

(i) $\Delta H^{\circ}_{298}$, $\Delta S^{\circ}_{298}$ and $\Delta G^{\circ}_{298}$ for the reaction of 2,2′,2″-triaminotriethylamine (tren, $= N(CH_2CH_2NH_2)_3$) with the aqueous ions $Mn^{2+}$, $Fe^{2+}$ and $Ni^{2+}$ are listed in Table 39. Tren is a quadridentate ligand, and the reaction is therefore

$$M(H_2O)_6^{2+}(aq) + tren(aq) \rightleftharpoons M(tren)(H_2O)_2^{2+}(aq) + 4H_2O(l).$$

**Table 39** Thermodynamic Data for the Formation of $M(tren)(H_2O)_2^{2+}$ and $M(en)_2(H_2O)_2^{2+}$ in Aqueous Solution

| | $\Delta H^{\circ}_{298}$ /(kJ mol$^{-1}$) | $\Delta S^{\circ}_{298}$ /(J K$^{-1}$ mol$^{-1}$) | $T\Delta S^{\circ}_{298}$ /(kJ mol$^{-1}$) | $\Delta G^{\circ}_{298}$ /(kJ mol$^{-1}$) |
|---|---|---|---|---|
| $M(tren)(H_2O)_2^{2+}$ | | | | |
| Mn | −12·6 | +69 | +20·7 | −33·3 |
| Fe | −26·4 | +77 | +23·1 | −49·5 |
| Ni | −63·4 | +92 | +27·5 | −90·9 |
| $M(en)_2(H_2O)_2^{2+}$ | | | | |
| Mn | −25·2 | +8 | +2·5 | −27·7 |
| Fe | −43·5 | 0 | 0·0 | −43·5 |
| Ni | −76·4 | +13 | +3·8 | −80·2 |

Also listed in Table 39 are the corresponding thermodynamic data for the reactions in which two moles of ethylenediamine (en) react in place of one mole of tren, that is for the reaction

$$M(H_2O)_6^{2+}(aq) + 2en(aq) \rightleftharpoons M(en)_2(H_2O)_2^{2+}(aq) + 4H_2O(l).$$

It is noteworthy that for the tren complexes the enthalpy changes are *less exothermic* than those for the en complexes by 13 to 17 kJ mol$^{-1}$, and this has been attributed (P. Paoletti, M. Ciampolini and L. Sacconi, 1964) partly to the steric strain resulting from the presence of three chelate rings (as opposed to only two in the en complexes), and partly to the inherently lower strength of the M—N bond when N is a *tertiary* nitrogen atom (as opposed to the *primary* nitrogen atom in en).

The entropy changes, however, are *more positive* for the tren complexes, because four water molecules are liberated from the aquo complex by a *single* tren molecule whereas *two* en molecules are required to produce the same effect. The tren reaction therefore results in a relatively greater increase in the number of free (uncomplexed) molecules. It can be seen from the $\Delta G^\circ$ values that the tren complexes are the more stable – their formation involves greater free energy losses – and this is essentially a consequence of the more favourable entropy effect.

(ii) The above example illustrates what has been called the 'chelate effect', that is the enhanced stability of chelated complexes compared with complexes which have no (or fewer) chelate rings. A further example is as follows. The data of Table 40 refer to the replacement of two coordinated pyridine molecules by a single bidentate dipyridyl molecule (which forms a chelate ring) in the reaction

$$M(py)_2^{2+}(aq) + dipy(aq) \rightleftharpoons M(dipy)^{2+}(aq) + 2py(aq)$$

Where   py =   (pyridine)   and   dipy =   (2,2'-dipyridyl).

The positive entropy changes are similar for all four metals and are associated primarily with the increase in the number of uncomplexed mole-

**Table 40**  Thermodynamic Data for the Reaction
$M(py)_2^{2+}(aq) + dipy(aq) \rightleftharpoons M(dipy)^{2+}(aq) + 2py(aq)$

| | $\Delta H^\circ_{298}$ /(kJ mol$^{-1}$) | $\Delta S^\circ_{298}$ /(J K$^{-1}$ mol$^{-1}$) | $T \Delta S^\circ_{298}$ /(kJ mol$^{-1}$) | $\Delta G^\circ_{298}$ /(kJ mol$^{-1}$) |
|---|---|---|---|---|
| Mn$^{II}$ | +2·0 | +24 | +6·4 | −4·4 |
| Ni$^{II}$ | −11·6 | +19 | +5·6 | −17·2 |
| Cu$^{II}$ | −10·2 | +14 | +4·3 | −14·5 |
| Zn$^{II}$ | −0·5 | +20 | +5·9 | −6·4 |

cules. In the case of manganese and zinc complexes, the enthalpy changes $(\Delta H^\circ_{298})$ are very small. For the nickel and copper complexes, however, negative values of $\Delta H^\circ_{298}$ contribute significantly to the over-all free energy decrease and have been attributed (G. Atkinson and J. E. Bauman, 1963) principally to the fact that dipyridyl produces a greater crystal field stabilization effect than pyridine. In the case of $Mn^{II}$ and $Zn^{II}$, which have $d^5$ and $d^{10}$ configurations, no crystal field stabilization is possible. (See section 3.5.1.)

# References

AHRENS, L. H. (1952), *Geochimica et Cosmochimica Acta*, vol. 2, no. 3, pp. 155–69.

ATKINSON, G., and BAUMAN, J. E., Jr. (1963), *Inorganic Chemistry*, vol. 2, no. 1, pp. 64–7.

COBBLE, J. W. (1953), *Journal of Chemical Physics*, vol. 21, no. 9, pp. 1443–6.

COUTURE, A. M., and LAIDLER, K. J. (1957), *Canadian Journal of Chemistry*, vol. 35, no. 3, pp. 202–6.

CROSSLEY, R. J. S. (1964), *Proceedings of the Physical Society*, vol. 83, pp. 375–89.

HALLIWELL, H. F., and NYBURG, S. C. (1963), *Transactions of the Faraday Society*, vol. 59, pp. 1126–40.

HINZE, J., and JAFFÉ, H. H. (1962), *Journal of the American Chemical Society*, vol. 84, no. 4, pp. 540–46.

KAPUSTINSKII, A. F. (1956), *Quarterly Reviews*, Chemical Society, London, vol. 10, no. 3, pp. 283–94.

KUBASCHEWSKI, O., EVANS, E. L., and ALCOCK, C. B. (1967), *Metallurgical Thermochemistry*, 4th edn, Pergamon Press.

LADD, M. F. C., and LEE, W. H. (1961a), *Journal of Inorganic and Nuclear Chemistry*, vol. 20, no. 1/2, pp. 163–5.

LADD, M. F. C., and LEE, W. H. (1961b), *Journal of Inorganic and Nuclear Chemistry*, vol. 21, no. 3/4, pp. 216–20.

LATIMER, W. M. (1952), *Oxidation Potentials*, 2nd edn, Prentice Hall.

LENNARD-JONES, J., and INGHAM, A. E. (1925), *Proceedings of the Royal Society*, series A, vol. 107, no. 744, pp. 636–53.

LEWIS, G. N., and RANDALL, M. (1961), *Thermodynamics*, 2nd edn revised by K. S. Pitzer and L. Brewer, McGraw-Hill.

MAYER, J. E. (1933a), *Journal of Chemical Physics*, vol. 1, no. 4, pp. 270–79.

MAYER, J. E. (1933b), *Journal of Chemical Physics*, vol. 1, no. 5, pp. 327–34.

MAYER, J. E., and LEVY, R. B. (1933), *Journal of Chemical Physics*, vol. 1, no. 9, pp. 647–8.

McCOUBREY, J. C. (1955), *Transactions of the Faraday Society*, vol. 51, pp. 743–7.

MOORE, C. E. (1949), *Atomic Energy Levels*, National Bureau of Standards (U.S.A.) Circular 467, vol. 1.

MOORE, C. E. (1952), *Atomic Energy Levels*, National Bureau of Standards (U.S.A.) Circular 467, vol. 2.

MOORE, C. E. (1958), *Atomic Energy Levels*, National Bureau of Standards (U.S.A.) Circular 467, vol. 3.

NOYES, R. M. (1962), *Journal of the American Chemical Society*, vol. 84, no. 4, pp. 513–22.

NOYES, R. M. (1963), *Journal of Chemical Education*, vol. 40, no. 1, pp. 2–10.

PAOLETTI, P., CIAMPOLINI, M., and SACCONI, L. (1963), *Journal of the Chemical Society*, pp. 3589–93.

PAULING, L. (1927), *Proceedings of the Royal Society*, series A, vol. 114, no. 767, pp. 181–211.

PAULING, L. (1960), *Nature of the Chemical Bond*, 3rd edn, Oxford University Press.

PHILLIPS, C. S. G., and WILLIAMS, R. J. P. (1965), *Inorganic Chemistry*, Oxford University Press.

PITZER, K. S. (1937), *Journal of the American Chemical Society*, vol. 59, no. 11, pp. 2367–71.

POWELL, R. E., and LATIMER, W. M. (1951), *Journal of Chemical Physics*, vol. 19, no. 9, pp. 1139–41.

WADDINGTON, T. C. (1959), in H. J. Emeleus and A. G. Sharpe (eds.) *Advances in Inorganic Chemistry and Radiochemistry*, Academic Press, vol. 1, pp. 157–221.

# Index